S0-BRY-872

Engineering

Math +

1st ed — mostly
+ to U. Mi.
author —
copy on net to
fifty —

565

5193106098
24-4

MATHEMATICAL MONOGRAPHS

EDITED BY

Mansfield Merriman and Robert S. Woodward.

Octavo, Cloth.

No. 1. **History of Modern Mathematics.** By DAVID EUGENE SMITH. $1.00 *net*.

No. 2. **Synthetic Projective Geometry.** By GEORGE BRUCE HALSTED. $1.00 *net*.

No. 3. **Determinants.** By LAENAS GIFFORD WELD. $1.00 *net*.

No. 4. **Hyperbolic Functions.** By JAMES McMAHON. $1.00 *net*.

No. 5. **Harmonic Functions.** By WILLIAM E. BYERLY. $1.00 *net*.

No. 6. **Grassmann's Space Analysis.** By EDWARD W. HYDE. $1.00 *net*.

No. 7. **Probability and Theory of Errors.** By ROBERT S. WOODWARD. $1.00 *net*.

No. 8. **Vector Analysis and Quaternions.** By ALEXANDER MACFARLANE. $1.00 *net*.

No. 9. **Differential Equations.** BY WILLIAM WOOLSEY JOHNSON. $1.00 *net*.

No. 10. **The Solution of Equations.** By MANSFIELD MERRIMAN. $1.00 *net*.

No. 11. **Functions of a Complex Variable.** By THOMAS S. FISKE. $1.00 *net*.

No. 12. **The Theory of Relativity.** By ROBERT D. CARMICHAEL. $1.00 *net*.

No. 13. **The Theory of Numbers.** By ROBERT D. CARMICHAEL. $1.00 *net*.

No. 14. **Algebraic Invariants.** By LEONARD E. DICKSON. $1.25 *net*.

No. 15. **Mortality Laws and Statistics.** By ROBERT HENDERSON. $1.25 *net*.

No. 16. **Diophantine Analysis.** By ROBERT D. CARMICHAEL. $1.25 *net*.

No. 17. **Ten British Mathematicians.** By ALEXANDER MACFARLANE. $1.25 *net*.

No. 18. **Elliptic Integrals.** By HARRIS HANCOCK. $1.25 *net*.

No. 19. **Empirical Formulas.** By THEODORE R. RUNNING. $1.40 *net*.

PUBLISHED BY

JOHN WILEY & SONS, Inc., NEW YORK.

CHAPMAN & HALL, Limited, LONDON.

MATHEMATICAL MONOGRAPHS

EDITED BY

MANSFIELD MERRIMAN AND ROBERT S. WOODWARD

No. 19

EMPIRICAL FORMULAS

BY

THEODORE R. RUNNING

ASSOCIATE PROFESSOR OF MATHEMATICS, UNIVERSITY OF MICHIGAN

FIRST EDITION

NEW YORK

JOHN WILEY & SONS, INC.

LONDON: CHAPMAN & HALL, LIMITED

1917

DEP'T TERRESTRIAL MAGNETISM,
CARNEGIE INSTITUTION,
WASHINGTON, D, C.

19324

DISCARDED BY
D.T.M. LIBRARY

COPYRIGHT, 1917,

BY

THEODORE R. RUNNING

PRESS OF
BRAUNWORTH & CO.
BOOK MANUFACTURERS
BROOKLYN, N. Y.

PREFACE

THIS book is the result of an attempt to answer a number of questions which frequently confront engineers. So far as the author is aware no other book in English covers the same ground in an elementary manner.

It is thought that the method of determining the constants in formulas by the use of the straight line alone leaves little to be desired from the point of view of simplicity. The approximation by this method is close enough for most problems arising in engineering work. Even when the Method of Least Squares must be employed the process gives a convenient way of obtaining approximate values.

For valuable suggestions and criticisms the author here expresses his thanks to Professors Alexander Ziwet and Horace W. King.

T. R. R.

UNIVERSITY OF MICHIGAN, 1917.

3

CONTENTS

EMPIRICAL FORMULAS

INTRODUCTION

In the results of most experiments of a quantitative nature, two variables occur, such as the relation between the pressure and the volume of a certain quantity of gas, or the relation between the elongation of a wire and the force producing it. On plotting the sets of corresponding values it is found, if they really depend on each other, that the points so located lie approximately on a smooth curve.

In obtaining a mathematical expression which shall represent the relation between the variables so plotted there may be two distinct objects in view, one being to determine the physical law underlying the observed quantities, the other to obtain a simple formula, which may or may not have a physical basis, and by which an approximate value of one variable may be computed from a given value of the other variable.

In the first case correctness of form is a necessary consideration. In the second correctness of form is generally considered subordinate to simplicity and convenience. It is with the latter of these (Empirical Formulas) that this volume is mostly concerned.

The problem of determining the equation to be used is really an indeterminate one; for it is clear that having given a set of corresponding values of two variables a number of equations can be found which will represent their relation approximately.

Let the coördinates of the points in Fig. 1 represent different sets of corresponding values of two observed quantities, x and y. If the points be joined by segments of straight lines the broken line thus formed will represent to the eye, roughly, the relation between the quantities.

It is reasonable to suppose, however, that the irregular distribution of the points is due to errors in the observations, and that a smooth curve drawn to conform approximately to the distribution of the points will more nearly represent the true relation between the variables. But here we are immediately confronted with a difficulty. Which curve shall we select? *a*

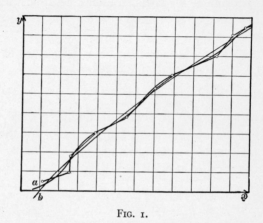

FIG. 1.

or *b*? or one of a number of other curves which might be drawn to conform quite closely to the distribution of the points?

In determining the form of curve to be used reliance must be largely placed upon intuition and upon knowledge of the experiments performed.

The problem of determining a simple equation which will represent as nearly as possible the curve selected is by far the more difficult one.

Ordinarily the equation to be used will be derived from a consideration of the data without the intermediate step of drawing the curve.

Unfortunately, there is no general method which will give the best form of equation to be used. There are, however, a number of quite simple tests which may be applied to a set of data, and which will enable us to make a fairly good choice of equation.

The first five chapters deal with the application of these tests and the evaluation of the constants entering into the equations. Chapter VI is devoted to the evaluation of the constants in empirical formulas by the Method of Least Squares. In Chapter VII formulas for interpolation are developed and their applications briefly treated. Chapter VIII is devoted to approximate formulas for areas, volumes, centroids, moments of inertia, and a number of examples are given to illustrate their application.

Figs. I to XX at the end of the book show a few of the forms of curves represented by the different formulas.

A few definitions may be added.

Arithmetical Series. A series of numbers each of which, after the first, is derived from the preceding by the addition of a constant number is called an *arithmetical series.* The constant number is called the *common difference*

$$6, \quad 6.3, \quad 6.6, \quad 6.9, \quad 7.2, \quad 7.5 \cdots$$
and
$$18.0, \quad 15.8, \quad 13.6, \quad 11.4, \quad 9.2 \cdots$$

are arithmetical series. In the first the common difference is .3, and in the second the common difference is -2.2.

Geometrical Series. A series of numbers each term of which, after the first, is derived by multiplying the preceding by some constant multiplier is called a *geometrical series.* The constant, multiplier is called the *ratio.*

$$1.3, \quad 2.6, \quad 5.2, \quad 10.4, \quad 20.8, \quad 41.6 \cdots$$
and
$$100, \quad 20, \quad 4, \quad .8, \quad .16, \quad .032 \cdots$$

are geometrical series. In the first the ratio is 2, and in the second it is .2.

Differences are frequently employed and their meaning can best be brought out by an example.

x	y	Δy	$\Delta^2 y$	$\Delta^3 y$	$\Delta^4 y$
1	10.2				
2	11.1	0.9			
			0.2		
3	12.2	1.1		0.0	
			0.2		1.2
4	13.5	1.3		1.2	
			1.4		−3.5
5	16.2	2.7		−2.3	
			−0.9		2.4
6	18.0	1.8		0.1	
			−0.8		2.7
7	19.0	1.0		2.8	
			2.0		
8	22.0	3.0			

In the table corresponding values of x and y are given in the first two columns. In the third column are given the values of the first differences. These are designated by Δy. The first value in the third column is obtained by subtracting the first value of y from the second value. The column of second differences, designated by $\Delta^2 y$, is obtained from the values of Δy in the same way that the column of first differences were obtained from the values of y. The method of obtaining the higher differences is evident.

CHAPTER I

I. $y = a + bx + cx^2 + dx^3 + \ldots + qx^n$

Values of x form an arithmetical series and $\Delta^n y$ constant.

IN a tensile test of a mild steel bar, the following observations were made (Low's Applied Mechanics, p. 188): Diameter of bar, unloaded, 0.748 inch, W = load in tons, x = elongation in inches, on a length of 8 inches.

W	1	2	3	4	5	6
x	0.0014	0.0027	0.0040	0.0055	0.0068	0.0082
Δx	0.0013	0.0013	0.0015	0.0013	0.0014	

Plotting W and x, Fig. 2, it is observed that the points lie very nearly on a straight line.* Indeed, the fit is so good that it may be almost concluded that there exists a linear relation, between W and x. From the figure it is found that the slope of the line is 0.00137 and that it passes through the origin. The relation between W and x is therefore expressed by the equation

$$x = 0.00137 W.$$

The observed values of x and the values computed by the above formula are given in the table below.

W	Observed x	Computed x
1	0.0014	0.00137
2	0.0027	0.00274
3	0.0040	0.00411
4	0.0055	0.00548
5	0.0068	0.00685
6	0.0082	0.00822

* By the use of a fine thread the position of the line can be determined quite readily.

13

The agreement between the observed and the computed values is seen to be quite good. It is to be noted, however, that the formula can not be used for computing values of x outside

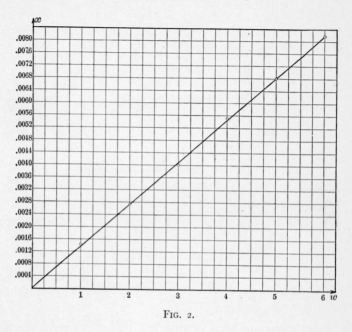

FIG. 2.

the elastic limit. In the experiment 6 tons was the load at the elastic limit.

It is not necessary to plot the points to determine whether they lie approximately on a straight line or not. Consider the general equation of the straight line

$$y = mx + k.$$

Starting from any value of x, give to x an increment, Δx, and y will have a corresponding increment, Δy.

$$y + \Delta y = m(x + \Delta x) + k;$$

$$y = mx + k;$$

$$\Delta y = m\Delta x.$$

From this it is seen that, in the case of a straight line, if the increment of one of the variables is constant, the increment of the other will also be constant.

From the table it is observed that the successive values of W differ by unity, and that the difference between the successive values of x is very nearly constant. Hence the relation between the variables is expressed approximately by

$$x = mW + k,$$

where m and k have the values determined graphically from the figure.

By the nature of the work it is readily seen that the graphical determination of the constants will be only approximate under the most favorable conditions, and should be employed only when the degree of approximation required will warrant it. Satisfactory results can be obtained only by exercising great care. Carelessness in a few details will often render the results useless. Understanding how a graphical process is to be carried out is essential to good work; but not less important is the practice in applying that knowledge.

In experimental results involving two variables the values of the independent variable are generally given in an arithmetical series. Indeed, it is seldom that results in any other form occur. It will be seen, however, that in many cases where the values of the independent variable are given in an arithmetical series it will be convenient to select these values in a geometrical series.

As a special case consider the equation

$$y = 2 - 3x + x^2.$$

If an increment be assigned to x, y will have a corresponding increment. The values of x and y are represented in the table below. Δy stands for the number obtained by subtracting any value of y from the succeeding value. $\Delta^2 y$ stands for the number obtained by subtracting any value of Δy from its succeeding value. The values of x have the common difference 0.5.

x	0.5	1.0	1.5	2.0	2.5	3.0	3.5	4.0
y	0.75	0.00	−0.25	0.00	0.75	2.00	3.75	6.00
Δy	−0.75	−0.25	0.25	0.75	1.25	1.75	2.25	
$\Delta^2 y$	0.50	0.50	0.50	0.50	0.50	0.50		

The values $\Delta^2 y$, which we call the second differences, are constant.

These differences could equally well have been computed as follows:

$$y = 2 - 3x + x^2,$$

$$y + \Delta y = 2 - 3(x + \Delta x) + (x + \Delta x)^2,$$

$$\Delta y = -3(\Delta x) + 2x(\Delta x) + (\Delta x)^2,$$

$$\Delta y + \Delta^2 y = -3(\Delta x) + 2(x + \Delta x)(\Delta x) + (\Delta x)^2,$$

$$\Delta^2 y = 2(\Delta x)^2 = 0.5 \text{ since } \Delta x = 0.5.$$

From this it is seen that whatever the value of Δx (in $y = 2 - 3x + x^2$) the second differences of the values of y are constant.

Consider now the general case where the nth differences are constant. For convenience the values of y and the successive differences will be arranged in columns. The notation used is self-explanatory.

$$
\begin{array}{llll}
y_1 & & & \\
& \Delta y_1 & & \\
y_2 & & \Delta^2 y_1 & \\
& \Delta y_2 & & \Delta^3 y_1 \qquad\qquad \text{etc.,}\\
y_3 & & \Delta^2 y_2 & \qquad \Delta^4 y_1 \\
& \Delta y_3 & & \Delta^3 y_2 \qquad\qquad \text{etc.,}\\
y_4 & & \Delta^2 y_3 & \qquad \Delta^4 y_2 \\
& \Delta y_4 & & \Delta^3 y_3 \qquad\qquad \text{etc.,}\\
y_5 & & \Delta^2 y_4 & \qquad \cdots \\
& \Delta y_5 & & \cdots \\
y_6 & & \cdots & \\
& \cdots & & \\
\cdots & & &
\end{array}
$$

From the above it is clear that

$$y_2 = y_1 + \Delta y_1,$$

$$\begin{aligned} y_3 &= y_2 + \Delta y_2, \\ &= y_1 + \Delta y_1 + \Delta(y_1 + \Delta y_1). \\ &= y_1 + 2\Delta y_1 + \Delta^2 y_1. \end{aligned}$$

$$\begin{aligned} y_4 &= y_3 + \Delta y_3, \\ &= y_1 + 2\Delta y_1 + \Delta^2 y_1 + \Delta(y_1 + 2\Delta y_1 + \Delta^2 y_1), \\ &= y_1 + 3\Delta y_1 + 3\Delta^2 y_1 + \Delta^3 y_1. \end{aligned}$$

$$\begin{aligned} y_5 &= y_4 + \Delta y_4, \\ &= y_1 + 3\Delta y_1 + 3\Delta^2 y_1 + \Delta^3 y_1 + \Delta(y_1 + 3\Delta y_1 + 3\Delta^2 y_1 + \Delta^3 y_1) \\ &= y_1 + 4\Delta y_1 + 6\Delta^2 y_1 + 4\Delta^3 y_1 + \Delta^4 y_1. \end{aligned}$$

In the above equations the coefficients follow the law of the binomial theorem. Assuming that the law holds for y_k it will be proved that it holds for y_{k+1}.

By hypothesis

$$y = y_1 + (k-1)\Delta y_1 + \frac{(k-1)(k-2)}{\underline{|2}}\Delta^2 y_1$$
$$+ \frac{(k-1)(k-2)(k-3)}{\underline{|3}}\Delta^3 y_1 + \text{etc.} \quad . \quad . \quad . \quad . \quad (1)$$

If this equation is true, then

$$y_{k+1} = y_1 + (k-1)\Delta y_1 + \frac{(k-1)(k-2)}{\underline{|2}}\Delta^2 y_1$$
$$+ \frac{(k-1)(k-2)(k-3)}{\underline{|3}}\Delta^3 y_1 + \text{etc.}$$
$$+ \Delta\left[y_1 + (k-1)\Delta y_1 + \frac{(k-1)(k-2)}{\underline{|2}}\Delta^2 y_1 \right.$$
$$\left. + \frac{(k-1)(k-2)(k-3)}{\underline{|3}}\Delta^3 y_1 + \text{etc.} \right]$$
$$= y_1 + k\Delta y_1 + \frac{k(k-1)}{\underline{|2}}\Delta^2 y + \frac{k(k-1)(k-2)}{\underline{|3}}\Delta^3 y$$
$$+ \frac{k(k-1)(k-2)(k-3)}{\underline{|4}}\Delta^4 y_1 + \text{etc.}$$

This is the same law as expressed in the former equation, and therefore, if the law holds for y_k, it must also hold for y_{k+1}. But we have shown that it holds for y_4, and therefore, it must hold for y_5.

Since it holds for y_5 it will hold for y_6. By this process it is proved that the law holds in general.

If now the first differences are constant the second and higher differences will be zero, and from (1)

$$y_k = y_1 + (k-1)\Delta y_1.$$

If the second differences are constant the third and higher differences will be zero, and it follows from (1) that

$$y_k = y_1 + (k-1)\Delta y_1 + \frac{(k-1)(k-2)}{\underline{|2}}\Delta^2 y_1.$$

In general, then, if the nth differences are constant

$$y_k = y_1 + (k-1)\Delta y_1 + \frac{(k-1)(k-2)}{\underline{|2}}\Delta^2 y_1 + \frac{(k-1)(k-2)(k-3)}{\underline{|3}}\Delta^3 y_1$$

$$+ \ldots + \frac{(k-1)(k-2)(k-3)(k-4) \ldots (k-n)}{\underline{|n}}\Delta^n y_1. \quad (2)$$

The law requires that the values of x form an arithmetical series, and hence

$$x_k = x_1 + (k-1)\Delta x;$$

from which follows

$$k = \frac{x_k - x_1}{\Delta x} + 1. \quad \ldots \ldots \ldots \quad (3)$$

Substituting this value of k in equation (2) it is found that the right-hand member becomes a rational integral function of x_k of the nth degree. Equation (2) takes the form

$$y_k = a + bx_k + cx_k^2 + dx_k^3 + \ldots + qx_k^n.$$

Since x_k and y_k are any two corresponding values of x and y the subscripts may be dropped and there results the following law:

If two variables, x and y, are so related that when values of x are taken in an arithmetical series the nth differences of the corresponding values of y are constant, the law connecting the variables is expressed by the equation

I
$$y = a + bx + cx^2 + dx^3 + \ldots + qx^n.$$

The nth differences of the values of y obtained from observations are seldom if ever constant. If, however, the nth differences approximate to a constant it may be concluded that the relation between the variables is fairly well represented by I.

As an illustration consider the data given on page 131 of Merriman's Method of Least Squares. The table gives the velocities of water in the Mississippi River at different depths for the point of observation chosen, the total depth being taken as unity.

	v	Δv	$\Delta^2 v$	$\Delta^3 v$	$\Delta^4 v$	$\Delta^5 v$
At surface......	3.1950					
0.1 depth.....	3.2299	+349	−116			
0.2 "	3.2532	+233	−154	− 38	+ 18	
0.3 "	3.2611	+ 79	−174	− 20	+ 55	+ 37
0.4 "	3.2516	− 95	−139	+ 35	−137	−192
0.5 "	3.2282	−234	−241	−102	+277	+414
0.6 "	3.1807	−475	− 66	+175	−240	−517
0.7 "	3.1266	−541	−131	− 65	+ 33	+273
0.8 "	3.0594	−672	−163	− 32		
0.9 "	2.9759	−835				

From the above table it is seen that the second differences are more nearly constant than any of the other series of differences. Of equations of form I,

$$y = a + bx + cx^2,$$

where x stands for depth and y for velocity, will best represent the law connecting the two variables. It should be emphasized, however, that the fact that the second differences are nearly constant does not show that I is the correct form of equation to be used. It only shows that the equation selected will represent fairly well the relation between the two variables.

It might be suggested that if an equation of form I with ten constants were selected these constants could be so determined that the ten sets of values given in the table would satisfy the equation. To determine these constants we would substitute in turn each set of values in the selected equation and from the ten equations thus formed compute the values of the constants. But we would have no assurance that the equation so formed would better express the law than the equation of the second degree.

For the purpose of determining the approximate values of the constants in the equation

$$y = a + bx + cx^2 \qquad \ldots \ldots \ldots \quad (1)$$

from the data given proceed in the following way:

$$\text{Let } x = X + x_0,$$

$$y = Y + y_0,$$

where x_0 and y_0 are any corresponding values of x and y taken from the data. The equation becomes

$$Y + y_0 = a + b(X + x_0) + c(X + x_0)^2$$

$$= a + bx_0 + cx_0^2 + (b + 2cx_0)X + cX^2.$$

$$Y = (b + 2cx_0)X + cX^2; \qquad \ldots \ldots \quad (2)$$

since $y_0 = a + bx_0 + cx_0^2$. Dividing (2) by X it becomes

$$\frac{Y}{X} = b + 2cx_0 + cX. \qquad \ldots \ldots \ldots \quad (3)$$

This represents a straight line when X and $\dfrac{Y}{X}$ are taken as coördinates. The slope of the line is the value of c and the intercept the value of $b + 2cx_0$. The numerical work is shown in the table and the points represented by $\left(X, \dfrac{Y}{X} \right)$ are seen in Fig. 3. The value of c is found to be -0.76. When $x_0 = 0$, the intercept, 0.44 is the value of b. For $x = X$, the value of

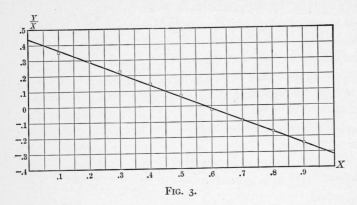

FIG. 3.

y_0 is taken from the table to be 3.1950, therefore each value of Y will be the corresponding value of y diminished by 3.1950.

x	y	X	Y	$\dfrac{Y}{X}$	$.44x - .76x^2$	$a = y - .44x$ $-.76x^2$	Computed y
.0	3.1950	.0	0.0000	....	0.0000	3.1950	3.1948
.1	3.2299	.1	0.0349	0.3490	0.0364	3.1935	3.2312
.2	3.2532	.2	0.0582	0.2910	0.0576	3.1956	3.2524
.3	3.2611	.3	0.0661	0.2203	0.0636	3.1975	3.2584
.4	3.2516	.4	0.0566	0.1415	0.0544	3.1972	3.2492
.5	3.2282	.5	0.0332	0.0664	0.0300	3.1982	3.2248
.6	3.1807	.6	−0.0143	−0.0238	−0.0096	3.1903	3.1852
.7	3.1266	.7	−0.0684	−0.0977	−0.0644	3.1910	3.1304
.8	3.0594	.8	−0.1356	−0.1695	−0.1344	3.1938	3.0604
.9	2.9759	.9	−0.2191	−0.2434	−0.2196	3.1955	2.9752

$$10)\underline{31.9476}$$
$$a = 3.1948$$

The numbers in column 6 were found after b and c were determined in Fig. 3. The sum of the numbers in the seventh column divided by ten gives the value of a. In the last column are written the values of y computed from the formula

$$y = 3.1948 + .44x - 76x^2. \quad \cdots \quad \cdots \quad (4)$$

$$\text{II.} \quad y = a + \frac{b}{x} + \frac{c}{x^2} + \frac{d}{x^3} + \cdots \frac{q}{x^n}.$$

Values of $\frac{1}{x}$ form an arithmetical series and $\Delta^n y$ are constant.

Another method of determining the constants is illustrated in the following example: Let it be required to find an equation which shall express approximately the relation between x and y having given the corresponding values in the first two columns of the table below.

1	2	3	4	5	6	7	8	9
x	y	$\frac{1}{x}$	x	y	Δy	$\Delta^2 y$	$y - \frac{2}{x^2}$	Computed y
1.0	4.000	1.0	1.000	4.00	−0.68	0.04	2.00	4.000
1.2	2.889	0.9	1.111	3.52	−0.64	0.03	1.50	2.889
1.4	2.163	0.8	1.250	2.68	−0.61	0.05	1.14	2.163
1.6	1.656	0.7	1.429	2.07	−0.56	0.05	0.87	1.656
1.8	1.284	0.6	1.667	1.51	−0.51	0.03	0.67	1.284
2.0	1.000	0.5	2.000	1.00	−0.48	0.04	0.50	1.000
2.2	0.777	0.4	2.500	0.52	−0.44	......	0.36	0.777
2.4	0.597	0.3	3.333	0.08	......	......	0.25	0.597

In column 3 are given values of $\frac{1}{x}$ in arithmetical series and the corresponding values of x and y are written in columns 4 and 5 of the table. The values of y were read from Fig. 4.

It is seen that the second differences of the values of y given in column 7 are nearly constant, and therefore the relation between the variables is represented approximately by the equation

$$y = a + b\left(\frac{1}{x}\right) + c\left(\frac{1}{x^2}\right). \quad \cdots \quad (5)$$

This becomes evident if x be replaced by $\frac{1}{x}$ in I. The law may then be stated:

If two variables, x and y, are so related that when values of $\frac{1}{x}$ are taken in arithmetical series the nth differences of the corre-

sponding values of y are constant, the law connecting the variables is expressed by the equation

II
$$y = a + \frac{b}{x} + \frac{c}{x^2} + \frac{d}{x^3} + \ldots \frac{q}{x^n}.$$

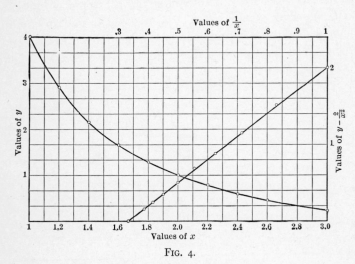

FIG. 4.

If in equation (5) $\dfrac{1}{x}$ be replaced by X, then

$$y = a + bX + cX^2, \quad \ldots \ldots \ldots \quad (6)$$

and

$$y + \Delta y = a + b(X + \Delta X) + c(X + \Delta X)^2.$$

By subtracting (6) from this equation

$$\Delta y = b\Delta X + 2c(\Delta X)X + c(\Delta X)^2; \quad \ldots \ldots \quad (7)$$

and from (7)

$$\Delta y + \Delta^2 y = b\Delta X + 2c(\Delta X)(X + \Delta X) + c(\Delta X)^2. \quad \ldots \quad (8)$$

Subtracting (7) from (8)

$$\Delta^2 y = 2c(\Delta X)^2;$$

$$c = \frac{\Delta^2 y}{2(\Delta X)^2}.$$

From column 7 it is seen that the average value of $\Delta^2 y$ is 0.04, and as ΔX was taken $-.1$,

$$c = \frac{0.04}{2\left(\frac{1}{100}\right)} = 2.$$

Writing the equation in the form

$$y - \frac{2}{x^2} = a + b\left(\frac{1}{x}\right),$$

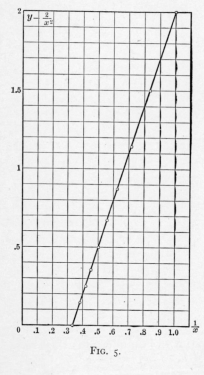

FIG. 5.

it is seen that it represents a straight line when $\frac{1}{x}$ and $y - \frac{2}{x^2}$ are the coördinates. From Fig. 5 b is found to be 3 and a to be -1. The formula is

$$y = -1 + 3\left(\frac{1}{x}\right) + 2\left(\frac{1}{x^2}\right).$$

The last column gives the values of y computed from this equation.

The following, taken from Saxelby's Practical Mathematics, page 134, gives the relation between the potential difference V and the current A in the electric arc. Length of arc $= 2$ mm., A is given in amperes, V in volts.

A	1.96	2.46	2.97	3.45	3.96	4.97	5.97	6.97	7.97	9.00
Observed V	50.25	48.70	47.90	47.50	46.80	45.70	45.00	44.00	43.60	43.50
$\frac{1}{A}$	.5102	.4065	.3367	.2899	.2525	.2012	.1675	.1435	.1255	.1111
Computed V	50.52	48.79	47.62	46.84	46.22	45.36	44.80	44.40	44.10	43.85

Fig. 6 shows V plotted to $\frac{1}{A}$ as abscissa. The slope of this line is 12.5 divided by .75 or 16.7. The intercept on the $V - ax$ is is 42. This gives for the relation between V and A

$$V = 42 + \frac{16.7}{A}.$$

Although the points in Fig. 6 do not follow the straight line very closely the agreement between the observed and the computed values of V is fairly good.

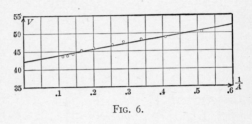

Fig. 6.

III. $\quad \frac{1}{y} = a + bx + cx^2 + dx^3 + \ldots + qx^n.$

Values of x form an arithmetical series and $\Delta^n \frac{1}{y}$ constant.

If two variables, x and y, are so related that when values of x are taken in an arithmetical series the nth differences of the corresponding values of $\frac{1}{y}$ are constant, the law connecting the variables is expressed by the equation

III $\qquad \frac{1}{y} = a + bx + cx^2 + dx^3 + \ldots + qx^n.$

This becomes evident by replacing y in I by $\frac{1}{y}$. The constants in III may be determined in the same way as they were in I.

IV. $\quad y^2 = a + bx + cx^2 + dx^3 + \ldots + qx^n.$

Values of x form an arithmetical series and $\Delta^n y^2$ constant.

If two variables, x and y, are so related that when values of x are taken in an arithmetical series the nth differences of the cor-

responding values of y^2 are constant, the law connecting the variables is expressed by the equation

IV $\qquad\qquad y^2 = a + bx + cx^2 + dx^3 + \ldots + qx^n.$

This also becomes evident from I by replacing y by y^2.

The method of obtaining the values of the constants in formulas III and IV is similar to that employed in formulas I and II and needs no particular discussion.

CHAPTER II

V. $y = ab^x$.

Values of x form an arithmetical series and the values of y a geometrical series.

If two variables, x and y, are so related that when values of x are taken in an arithmetical series the corresponding values of y form a geometrical series, the relation between the variables is expressed by the equation

$$V \qquad\qquad y = ab^x.$$

If the equation be written in the form

$$\log y = \log a + (\log b)x,$$

it is seen at once that if the values of x form an arithmetical series the corresponding values of $\log y$ will also form an arithmetical series, and, hence, the values of y form a geometrical series.

The law expressed by equation V has been called the compound interest law. If a represents the principal invested, b the amount of one dollar for one year, y will represent the amount at the end of x years.

The following example is an illustration under formula V.

In an experiment to determine the coefficient of friction, μ, for a belt passing round a pulley, a load of W lb. was hung from one end of the belt, and a pull of P lb. applied to the other end in order to raise the weight W. The table below gives corresponding values of α and μ, when α is the angle of contact between the belt and pulley measured in radians.

α	$\dfrac{\pi}{2}$	$\dfrac{2\pi}{3}$	$\dfrac{5\pi}{6}$	π	$\dfrac{7\pi}{6}$	$\dfrac{4\pi}{3}$	$\dfrac{3\pi}{2}$	$\dfrac{5\pi}{3}$	$\dfrac{11\pi}{6}$
P	5.62	6.93	8.52	10.50	12.90	15.96	19.67	24.24	29.94

27

The values of α form an arithmetical series and the values of P form very nearly a geometrical series, the ratio being 1.23. The law connecting the variables is

$$P = ab^{\alpha}.$$

The constants are determined graphically by first writing the equation in the form

$$\log P = \log a + \alpha \log b$$

and plotting the values of α and P on semi-logarithmic paper; or, using ordinary cross-section paper and plotting the values of α as abscissas and the values of $\log P$ as ordinates. Fig. 7 gives the points so located. The straight line which most nearly passes through all of the points has the slope .1733 and the intercept .4750. The slope is the value of $\log b$ and the intercept the value of $\log a$.

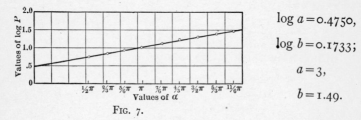

$$\log a = 0.4750,$$

$$\log b = 0.1733;$$

$$a = 3,$$

$$b = 1.49.$$

Fig. 7.

The formula expressing the relation between the variables is

$$P = 3(1.49)^{\alpha},$$

or

$$P = 3e^{.399\alpha}.$$

VI. $y = a + bc^x$.

Values of x form an arithmetical series and the values of Δy form a geometrical series.

If two variables, x and y, are so related that when values of x are taken in an arithmetical series the first differences of the values *of y form a geometrical series, the relation between the variables is expressed by the equation*

VI $$y = a + bc^z.$$

By the conditions stated the nth value of x will be

$$x_n = x_1 + (n-1)\,\Delta x,$$

and the series of first differences of the values of y will be

$$\Delta y_1, \quad \Delta y_1 r, \quad \Delta y_1 r^2, \quad \Delta y_1 r^3, \quad \Delta y_1 r^4 \ldots \Delta y_1 r^{n-2}.$$

The values of y will form the series

$$y_1, \quad y_1 + \Delta y_1, \quad y_1 + \Delta y_1 + r\Delta y_1, \quad y_1 + r\Delta y_1 + r^2\Delta y_1 \ldots$$

$$y_1 + \Delta y_1 + r\Delta y_1 + r^2\Delta y_1 + r^3\Delta y_1 + \ldots + r^{n-2}\Delta y_1.$$

The nth value of y will be represented by

$$y_n = y_1 + \Delta y_1\,\frac{1 - r^{n-1}}{1 - r}.$$

From the nth value of x

$$n - 1 = \frac{x_n - x_1}{\Delta x}.$$

Substituting this value in the above equation there is obtained

$$y_n = y_1 + \Delta y_1\frac{1 - r^{\frac{x_n - x_1}{\Delta x}}}{1 - r}$$
$$= a + bc^z,$$

where a stands for $y_1 + \dfrac{\Delta y_1}{1-r}$, b for $-\dfrac{\Delta y_1}{1-r}\,r^{\frac{-x_1}{\Delta x}}$, and c for $r^{\frac{1}{\Delta x}}$.

Let it be required to find the law connecting x and y having given the corresponding values in the first two lines of the table.

x	0	.1	.2	.3	.4	.5	.6	.7	.8	.9	1.0
y	1.300	1.440	1.597	1.774	1.974	2.198	2.452	2.737	3.060	3.423	3.830
Δy	0.140	0.157	0.177	0.200	0.224	0.254	0.285	0.323	0.363	0.407	
γ	1.300	1.439	1.597	1.774	1.973	2.198	2.452	2.738	3.059	3.421	3.830

Since the values of Δy form very nearly a geometrical series the relation between the variables is expressed approximately by

$$y = a + bc^x.$$

The constants in this formula can be determined graphically in either of two ways. First determine a and then subtract this value from each of the values of y giving a new relation

$$y - a = bc^x;$$

which may be written in the logarithmic form

$$\log (y - a) = \log b + x \log c,$$

and b and c determined as in Fig. 7; or, determine c first and plot c^x as abscissas to y as ordinate giving the straight line

$$y = a + b(c^x),$$

whose slope is b and whose intercept is a.

First Method. The determination of a is very simple. Select three points P, Q, and R on the curve drawn through the points represented by the data such that their abscissas form an arithmetical series. Fig. 8 shows the construction.

$$P \equiv (x_0,\ a + bc^{x_0});$$

$$Q \equiv (x_0 + \Delta x,\ a + bc^{x_0}c^{\Delta x});$$

$$R \equiv (x_0 + 2\Delta x,\ a + bc^{x_0}c^{2\Delta x}).$$

Select also two more points S and T such that

$$S \equiv (x_0 + \Delta x,\ a + bc^{x_0});$$

$$T \equiv (x_0 + 2\Delta x,\ a + bc^{x_0}c^{\Delta x}).$$

The equation of the line passing through Q and R is

$$y = \frac{bc^{x_0}c^{\Delta x}(c^{\Delta x} - 1)}{\Delta x}x - \frac{bc^{x_0}c^{\Delta x}(c^{\Delta x} - 1)}{\Delta x}(x_0 + \Delta x) + a + bc^{x_0}c^{\Delta x}. \quad (1)$$

The equation of the line through the points S and T is

$$y = \frac{bc^{x_0}(c^{\Delta x}-1)}{\Delta x}x - \frac{bc^{x_0}(c^{\Delta x}-1)}{\Delta x}(x_0+\Delta x)+a+bc^{x_0}. \quad . \quad (2)$$

These lines intersect in a point whose ordinate is a. For, multiplying equation (2) by $c^{\Delta x}$ and subtracting the resulting equation from (1) gives

$$(1-c^{\Delta x})y = (1-c^{\Delta x})a;$$

$$y = a.$$

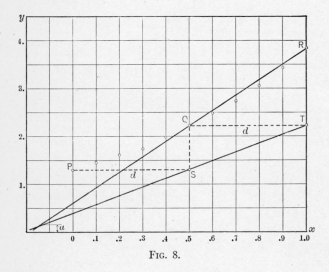

Fig. 8.

Fig. 8 gives the value of a equal to 0.2. The formula now becomes

$$\log (y-.2) = \log b + x \log c.$$

In Fig. 9 $\log (y-.2)$ is plotted to x as abscissa. The slope of the line is 0.5185 which is the value of $\log c$, hence c is equal to 3.3. The intercept is the ordinate of the first point or 0.0414, which is the logarithm of b, hence b is equal to 1.1. The formula is

$$y = 0.2 + 1.1(3.3)^x.$$

The last line in the table gives the values of y computed from this formula.

Second Method. For any point (x,y) the relation between x and y is expressed by

$$y=a+bc^x,$$

and for any other point $(x+\Delta x, y+\Delta y)$ by

$$y+\Delta y=a+bc^x c^{\Delta x}.$$

From these two equations is obtained

$$\Delta y=bc^x(c^{\Delta x}-1)$$

or

$$\log \Delta y=\log b(c^{\Delta x}-1)+x \log c.$$

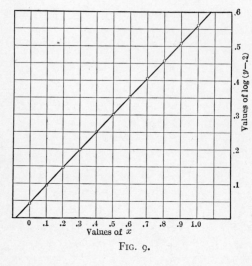

FIG. 9.

If now $\log \Delta y$ be plotted to x as abscissa a straight line is obtained whose slope is $\log c$. The value of c having been determined, the relation

$$y=a+b(c^x)$$

will represent a straight line provided y is plotted to c^x as abscissa. The slope of this line is b and its intercept a.

VII. $\log y=a+bc^x.$

Values of x form an arithmetical series and the values of $\Delta \log y$ form a geometrical series.

If two variables, x and y, are so related that when values of x are taken in an arithmetical series the first differences of the cor-

responding values of log y form a geometrical series, the relation between the variables is expressed by the equation

VII $$\log y = a + bc^x.$$

This is at once evident from VI when y is replaced by log y. The only difference in the proof is that instead of the series of differences of y the series of differences of log y is taken.

VIII. $y = a + bx + cd^x.$

Values of x form an arithmetical series and the values of $\Delta^2 y$ form a geometrical series.

If two variables, x and y, are so related that when values of x are taken in an arithmetical series the values of the second differences of the corresponding values of y form a geometrical series, the relation between the variables is expressed by the equation

VIII $$y = a + bx + cd^x.$$

The nth value of x is represented by

$$x_n = x_1 + (n - 1)\Delta x.$$

The values of y and the first and second differences may be arranged in columns

y_1		
	Δy_1	
y_2		$\Delta^2 y_1$
	Δy_2	
y_3		$\Delta^2 y_2$
	Δy_3	
y_4		$\Delta^2 y_3$
	Δy_4	
y_5		$\Delta^2 y_4$
	Δy_5	
y_6		etc.
	etc.	
etc.		

Since the second differences of y are to form a geometrical series they may be written

$$\Delta^2 y_1, \qquad r\Delta^2 y_1, \qquad r^2\Delta^2 y_1, \qquad r^3\Delta^2 y_1 \ldots r^{n-3}\Delta^2 y_1.$$

The series of first differences will then be

$$\Delta y_1, \quad \Delta y_1 + \Delta^2 y_1, \quad \Delta y_1 + \Delta^2 y_1 + r\Delta^2 y_1, \quad \Delta y_1 + \Delta^2 y_1 + r\Delta^2 y_1 + r^2\Delta^2 y_1$$

$$\cdot \quad \cdot \quad \cdot \quad \cdot \quad \cdot \quad \cdot \quad \cdot \quad \cdot \quad \cdot \quad \cdot$$

$$\Delta y_1 + \Delta^2 y_1 + r\Delta^2 y_1 + r^2\Delta^2 y_1 + \ldots + r^{n-3}\Delta^2 y_1.$$

The nth value of y will be equal to the first value plus all the first differences. For convenience the nth value of y is written in the table below.

$$y_n = y_1$$
$$+\Delta y_1$$
$$+\Delta y_1 + \Delta^2 y_1$$
$$+\Delta y_1 + \Delta^2 y_1 + r\Delta^2 y_1$$
$$+\Delta y_1 + \Delta^2 y_1 + r\Delta^2 y_1 + r^2\Delta^2 y_1$$
$$+\Delta y_1 + \Delta^2 y_1 + r\Delta^2 y_1 + r^2\Delta^2 y_1 + r^3\Delta^2 y_1$$

$$\cdot \quad \cdot \quad \cdot \quad \cdot \quad \cdot \quad \cdot \quad \cdot \quad \cdot \quad \cdot \quad \cdot$$

$$\cdot \quad \cdot \quad \cdot \quad \cdot \quad \cdot \quad \cdot \quad \cdot \quad \cdot \quad \cdot \quad \cdot$$

$$+\Delta y_1 + \Delta^2 y_1 + r\Delta^2 y_1 + r^2\Delta^2 y_1 + r^3\Delta^2 y_1 + \ldots + r^{n-3}\Delta^2 y_1.$$

Adding gives

$$y_n = y_1 + (n-1)\Delta y_1 + \Delta^2 y_1 \left[\frac{1-r}{1-r} + \frac{1-r^2}{1-r} + \frac{1-r^3}{1-r} + \frac{1-r^4}{1-r} \right. $$
$$\left. + \frac{1-r^5}{1-r} + \ldots + \frac{1-r^{n-2}}{1-r} \right].$$

The first two terms on the right-hand side represent the sum of all the terms in the first column of the value of y_n. The remaining terms contain the common factor $\Delta^2 y_1$. The terms inside the bracket are easily obtained when it is remembered that each line, omitting the first term, in the value of y form a geometrical series. It is easily seen that the value of y_n may be written

$$y_n = y_1 + (n-1)\Delta y_1 + \frac{\Delta^2 y_1}{1-r}(n-2) - \frac{\Delta^2 y_1}{1-r}(r + r^2 + r^3 + \ldots + r^{n-2})$$

$$= y_1 + (n-1)\Delta y_1 + \frac{\Delta^2 y_1}{1-r}(n-1) - \frac{\Delta^2 y_1}{1-r}\frac{1-r^{n-1}}{1-r}$$

$$= A + B(n-1) + Cr^{n-1};$$

where

$$A = y_1 - \frac{\Delta^2 y_1}{(1-r)^2}, \quad B = \Delta y_1 + \frac{\Delta^2 y_1}{1-r}, \text{ and } C = \frac{\Delta^2 y_1}{(1-r)^2}.$$

From the value of x_n is obtained

$$n - 1 = \frac{x_n - x_1}{\Delta x}.$$

Substituting this in the value of y_n it is found

$$y_n = A + B\frac{x_n - x_1}{\Delta x} + Cr^{\frac{x_n - x_1}{\Delta x}}$$

$$= a + bx_n + cd^{x_n}.$$

Since x_n and y_n stand for any set of corresponding values of x and y the resulting formula is

VIII $\qquad\qquad y = a + bx + cd^x.$

In the first two columns of the following table are given corresponding values of x and y from which it is required to find a formula representing the law connecting them.

x	y	Δy	$\Delta^2 y$	$\log \Delta^2 y$	$(2.00)^x$	$y - 1.01(2.00)^x$	Computed y
.0	1.500	.048	.023	-1.6383	1.000	.490	1.492
.2	1.548	.071	.026	-1.5850	1.149	.388	1.550
.4	1.619	.097	.028	-1.5528	1.320	.286	1.620
.6	1.716	.125	.034	-1.4685	1.517	.184	1.715
.8	1.841	.159	.039	-1.4089	1.742	.082	1.841
1.0	2.000	.198	.043	-1.3665	2.000	$-.020$	1.999
1.2	2.198	.241	.051	-1.2924	2.300	$-.125$	2.196
1.4	2.439	.292	.059	-1.2291	2.640	$-.227$	2.440
1.6	2.731	.351	.067	-1.1739	3.032	$-.331$	2.735
1.8	3.082	.418	....	....	3.482	$-.435$	3.085
2.0	3.500	....	....	....	4.000	$-.540$	3.506

Since the values of x form an arithmetical series and the second differences of the values of y form approximately a geometrical series, it is evident that the relation between the variables is fairly well represented by

$$y = a + bx + cd^x.$$

Taking the second difference

$$\Delta^2 y = c(d^{\Delta x} - 1)^2 d^x,$$

or

$$\log \Delta^2 y = \log c(d^{\Delta x} - 1)^2 + (\log d)x.$$

Plotting the logarithms of the second differences of y from the table to the values of x, Fig. 10, it is found that $\log d = .3000$

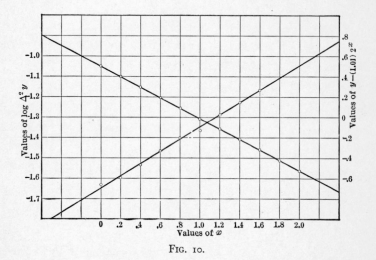

FIG. 10.

or $d = 1.995$, approximately 2. The intercept of this line, -1.6500, is equal to $\log c(d^{\Delta x} - 1)^2$.
Since

$$d = 2,$$

$$.02239 = c(2^{.2} - 1)^2,$$

$$c = 1.011.$$

Plotting $y-(1.01)2^x$ to x, Fig. 10, the values of a and b are found to be

$$a = 0.5,$$
$$b = -0.515.$$

The formula derived from the data is

$$y = 0.5 - 0.515x + (1.01)2^x.$$

In the last column of the table the values of y computed from the formula are written down. Comparing these values with the given values of y it is seen that the formula reproduces the values of y to a fair approximation.

IX. $y = 10^{a+bx+cx^2}$.

Values of x form an arithmetical series and $\Delta^2 \log y$ constant.

If two variables, x and y, are so related that when values of x are taken in an arithmetical series the second differences of the values of $\log y$ are constant, the relation between the variables is expressed by the equation

IX
$$y = 10^{a+bx+cx^2}.$$

This becomes evident from I when y is replaced by $\log y$.

$$\log y = a + bx + cx^2,$$

which represents a parabola when $\log y$ is plotted to x. The constants are determined in the same way as they were in formula I.

X. $y = ks^x g^{a^x}$.

Values of x form an arithmetical series and values of $\Delta^2 \log y$ form a geometrical series.

If two variables, x and y, are so related that when values of x are taken in an arithmetical series the second differences of the corresponding values of $\log y$ form a geometrical series, the relation between the variables is expressed by the equation

X
$$y = ks^x g^{a^x}.$$

This becomes evident by taking the logarithms of both sides and comparing the equations thus obtained with VIII. X becomes

$$\log y = \log k + (\log s)x + (\log g)d^x.$$

This is the same as VIII when y is replaced by $\log y$, a by $\log k$, b by $\log s$, and c by $\log g$.*

$$\text{XI.} \quad y = \frac{x}{a+bx+cx^2}.$$

Values of x form an arithmetical series and $\Delta^2 \frac{x}{y}$ are constant.

If two variables, x and y, are so related that when values of x are taken in an arithmetical series the second differences of the corresponding values of $\frac{x}{y}$ are constant, the relation between the variables is expressed by the equation

XI
$$y = \frac{x}{a+bx+cx^2}.$$

Clearing equation XI of fractions and dividing by y

$$\frac{x}{y} = a + bx + cx^2.$$

This is of the same form as I, and when $\frac{x}{y}$ is replaced by y the law stated above becomes evident.

If a is zero XI becomes

$$y = \frac{1}{b+cx},$$

which, by clearing of fractions and dividing by y, reduces to

$$\frac{1}{y} = b + cx,$$

a special case of III.

* For an extended discussion of X see Chapter VI of the Institute of Actuaries' Text Book by George King.

If c is zero XI becomes a special case of XVI, or

$$\frac{x}{y} = a + bx,$$

which is a straight line when $\frac{x}{y}$ is plotted to x.

Corresponding values of x and y are given in the table below, find a formula which will express approximately the relation between them.

x	y	$\frac{x}{y}$	$\Delta\frac{x}{y}$	$\Delta^2\frac{x}{y}$	X	Y	$\frac{Y}{X}$	$\frac{x}{y}-2.5x^2$	Computed y
0	0.000	.....	....	....	....	......	.....	......	0.000
.1	1.333	0.075	.100	.050	−.9	−2.703	3.003	.050	1.329
.2	1.143	0.175	.150	.050	−.8	−2.603	3.254	.075	1.140
.3	0.923	0.325	.200	.050	−.7	−2.453	3.504	.100	0.929
.4	0.762	0.525	.250	.050	−.6	−2.253	3.755	.125	0.760
.5	0.645	0.775	.300	.051	−.5	−2.003	4.006	.150	0.644
.6	0.558	1.075	.351	.049	−.4	−1.703	4.257	.175	0.558
.7	0.491	1.426	.400	.047	−.3	−1.352	4.507	.201	0.491
.8	0.438	1.826	.447	.058	−.2	−0.952	4.760	.226	0.438
.9	0.396	2.273	.505	.040	−.1	−0.503	5.030	.248	0.395
1.0	0.360	2.778	.545	.054	0	0.000	.....	......	0.360
1.1	0.331	3.323	.599	.056	.1	0.545	5.450	.298	0.331
1.2	0.306	3.922	.655	.051	.2	1.144	5.720	.332	0.305
1.3	0.284	4.577	.706	.035	.3	1.799	5.997	.352	0.284
1.4	0.265	5.283	.741	....	.4	2.505	6.262	.383	0.265
1.5	0.249	6.024	....	....	.5	3.246	6.492	.399	0.249

The values of x form an arithmetical series and since the second differences of $\frac{x}{y}$ are nearly constant the values of y will be fairly well represented by

$$y = \frac{x}{a+bx+cx^2},$$

or

$$\frac{x}{y} = a + bx + cx^2.$$

This represents a parabola when $\frac{x}{y}$ is plotted to x.

Let $X = x - 1$,

$$Y = \frac{x}{y} - 2.778.$$

From these equations are obtained

$$x = X + 1,$$

$$\frac{x}{y} = Y + 2.778.$$

The formula becomes

$$Y + 2.778 = a + b(X+1) + c(X+1)^2$$

$$= a + b + c + (b+2c)X + cX^2.$$

Since the new origin lies on the curve

$$a + b + c = 2.778,$$

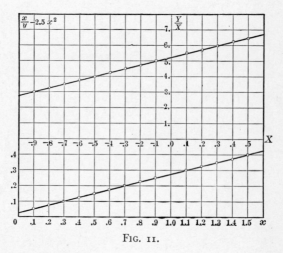

FIG. 11.

the equation reduces to

$$Y = (b+2c)X + cX^2,$$

or

$$\frac{Y}{X} = b + 2c + cX.$$

This represents a straight line when $\frac{Y}{X}$ is plotted to X. The value obtained for c from Fig. 11 is 2.5. The value of b could be obtained from the intercept of this line but the approximation will be better by plotting $\dfrac{x}{y} - 2.5x^2$ to x.   In this way is obtained the line

$$\frac{x}{y} - 2.5x^2 = a + bx.$$

From the lower part of Fig. 11 the values of a and b are found to be

$$a = .025,$$

$$b = .2525.$$

Substituting the values of the constants in XI the formula becomes

$$y = \frac{x}{.025 + .2525x + 2.5x^2}.$$

In the last column of the table the values of y computed from this equation are given and are seen to agree very well with the given values.

CHAPTER III

XII. $y = ax^b$.

Values of x form a geometrical series and the values of y form a geometrical series.

If two variables, x and y, are so related that when the values of x are taken in a geometrical series the corresponding values of y also form a geometrical series, the relation between the variables is expressed by the equation

XII $\qquad\qquad\qquad y = ax^b.$

From the conditions stated equations (a) and (b) are obtained.

$$x_n = x_1 r^{n-1}, \quad \cdots \cdots \cdots \quad (a)$$

$$y_n = y_1 R^{n-1}, \quad \cdots \cdots \cdots \quad (b)$$

where r is the ratio of any value of x to the preceding one and R is the ratio of any value of y to the preceding one.

Taking the logarithm of each member of (a)

$$\log x_n = \log x_1 + (n-1) \log r,$$

$$n - 1 = \frac{\log x_n - \log x_1}{\log r}.$$

Also by substituting this value of $n-1$ in the value of y_n in equation (b),

$$y_n = y_1 R^{\frac{\log x_n - \log x_1}{\log r}}$$

$$= y_1 R^{-\frac{\log x_1}{\log r}} \left(R^{\frac{1}{\log r}} \right)^{\log x_n}$$

$$= a(10^b)^{\log x_n}$$

$$= a 10^{\log x^b}$$

$$= ax^b,$$

where

$$a = y_1 R^{-\frac{\log x_n}{\log r}}$$

and

$$10^b = R^{\frac{1}{\log r}}.$$

The following data (Bach, Elastizität und Festigkeit) refer to a hollow cast-iron tube subject to a tensile stress; x represents the stress in kilogrammes per square centimeter of cross-section and y the elongation in terms of $\frac{1}{600}$ cm. as unit.

x......	9.79	20.02	40.47	60.92	81.37	101.82	204.00	408.57
y......	0.33	0.695	1.530	2.410	3.295	4.185	8.960	19.490
$\log x$...	0.9908	1.3014	1.6072	1.7847	1.9104	2.0078	2.3096	2.6113
$\log y$...	−0.4815	−0.1580	0.1847	0.3820	0.5178	0.6217	0.9523	1.2898
Comp.								
y....	0.324	0.714	1.541	2.416	3.323	4.252	9.132	19.600

Selecting the values of x which form a geometrical series, or nearly so, it is seen that the corresponding values of y form approximately a geometrical series, and, therefore, the relation between the variables is expressed by the equation

$$y = ax^b,$$

or

$$\log y = \log a + b \log x.$$

If now $\log y$ be plotted to $\log x$ the value of b will be the slope of the line and the intercept will be the value $\log a$. Fig. 12 gives $b = 1.1$. In computing the slope it must be remembered that the horizontal unit is twice as long as the vertical unit. The intercept is -1.5800 or $8.4200 - 10$, which is equal to $\log 0.0263$. The formula is

$$y = .0263 x^{1.1}.$$

The values of y computed from this equation are written in the last line of the table. They agree quite well with the observed values.

XIII. $y = a + b \log x + c \log^2 x$

Values of $\log x$ form an arithmetical series and $\Delta^2 y$ constant.

If two variables, x and y, are so related that when values of log x are taken in an arithmetical series the second differences of the corresponding values of y are constant the relation between the variables is expressed by the equation

XIII $\qquad\qquad y = a + b \log x + c \log^2 x.$

This becomes evident from I by replacing x by $\log x$. The law can also be stated as follows: If the values of x form a geo-

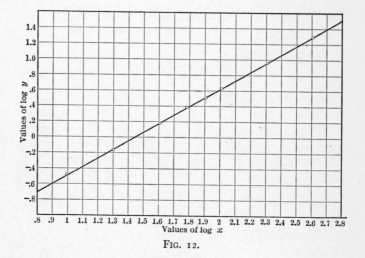

FIG. 12.

metrical series and the second differences of the corresponding values of y are constant the relation between the variables is expressed by the equation

$$y = a + b \log x + c \log^2 x.$$

If c is zero the formula becomes

$$y = a + b \log x,$$

which is V with x and y interchanged.

Formula XIII represents a parabola when y is plotted to $\log x$. The constants are determined in the same way as the constants in I.

$$\text{XIV.} \quad y = a + bx_{-}^{c}.$$

Values of x form a geometrical series and values of Δy form a geometrical series.

If two variables, x and y, are so related that when the values of x are taken in a geometrical series the first differences of the corresponding values of y form a geometrical series, the relation between the variables is expressed by the equation

XIV $\qquad\qquad y = a + bx^{c}.$

As in XII the nth value of x is

$$x_n = x_1 r^{n-1}. \quad \ldots \ldots \ldots \quad (c)$$

The series of first differences of y may be written

$$\Delta y_1, \qquad \Delta y_1 R, \qquad \Delta y_1 R^2, \qquad \Delta y_1 R^3 \ldots \Delta y_1 R^{n-2},$$

and the values of y are

$$y_1, \quad y_1 + \Delta y_1, \quad y_1 + \Delta y_1 + \Delta y_1 R, \quad y_1 + \Delta y_1 + \Delta y_1 R + \Delta y_1 R^2 \ldots$$

$$y_1 + \Delta y_1 + \Delta y_1 R + \Delta y_1 R^2 + \Delta y_1 R^3 + \ldots + \Delta y_1 R^{n-2}.$$

That is the nth value of y will be

$$y_n = y_1 + \Delta y_1 + \Delta y_1 R + \Delta y_1 R^2 + \Delta y_1 R^3 + \ldots + \Delta y_1 R^{n-2}$$

$$= y_1 + \Delta y_1 (1 + R + R^2 + R^3 + \ldots + R^{n-2})$$

$$= y_1 + \Delta y_1 \frac{1 - R^{n-1}}{1 - R}. \quad \ldots \ldots \ldots \ldots \quad (d)$$

Taking the logarithm of each member of (c),

$$\log x_n = \log x_1 + (n-1) \log r$$

$$n - 1 = \frac{\log x_n - \log x_1}{\log r}.$$

Substituting this value of $n-1$ in the nth value of y given in (d),

$$y_n = y_1 + \Delta y_1 \frac{1 - R^{\frac{\log x_n - \log x_1}{\log r}}}{1 - R}$$

$$= y_1 + \frac{\Delta y}{1 - R} - \frac{\Delta y}{1 - R} R^{-\frac{\log x_1}{\log r}} \left(R^{\frac{1}{\log r}} \right)^{\log x_n}$$

$$= a + b \left(10^c \right)^{\log x_n}$$

$$= a + b 10^{\log x_n^c}$$

$$= a + b x_n^c.$$

Let it be required to find the law connecting x and y having given the values in the first two lines of the table.

x	2	3	4	5	6	7	8
y	4.21	5.25	6.40	7.65	8.96	10.36	11.81
$\log x$	.3010	.4771	.6021	.6990	.7782	.8451	.9031
x	2	2.5	3.125	3.906	4.883	6.104	7.630
y	4.210	4.720	5.388	6.290	7.515	9.110	11.275
$\log x$	.3010	.3979	.4948	.5918	.6887	.7856	....
Δy	.510	.668	.902	1.225	1.595	2.165	....
$\log \Delta y$	−.2924	−.1752	−.0448	.0881	.2028	.3358	....
$y - 2.72$	1.49	2.53	3.68	4.93	6.24	7.64	9.09
$\log(y - 2.72)$	.1732	.4031	.5658	.6928	.7952	.8831	.9586
Computed y	4.21	5.25	6.41	7.65	8.98	10.36	11.81

In the fourth line values of x are given in a geometrical series with the ratio 1.25. In the fifth line are given the corresponding values of y read from Fig. 13. The first differences of the values of y are written in the seventh line. These differences form very nearly a geometrical series with the ratio 1.336. Since the ratio is nearly constant the law connecting x and y is fairly well represented by the equation

$$y = a + b x^c.$$

There are two methods which may be employed for determining the values of the constants, either one of which may serve as a check on the other.

First Method. Select three points, A, P, and Q on the curve, Fig. 13, such that their abscissas form a geometrical series and two other points, R and S, such that R has the same ordinate as A and the same abscissa as P, S the same ordinate as P and the same abscissa as Q. The points may be represented as follows:

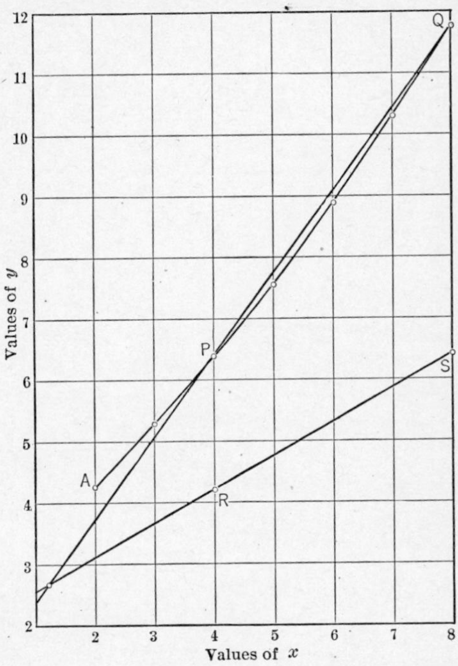

Values of y / Values of x

FIG. 13.

$$A \equiv (x_0,\ a + bx_0{}^c);$$

$$P \equiv (x_0 r,\ a + bx_0{}^c r^c);$$

$$Q \equiv (x_0 r^2,\ a + bx_0{}^c r^{2c});$$

$$R \equiv (x_0 r,\ a + bx_0{}^c);$$

$$S \equiv (x_0 r^2,\ a + bx_0{}^c r^c).$$

The equation of the line passing through P and Q is

$$y = \frac{bx_0{}^c r^c (r^c - 1)}{x_0 r (r - 1)} x + a - \frac{bx_0{}^c r^c (r^c - r)}{r - 1}.$$

The equation of the line passing through the points R and S is

$$y = \frac{bx_0{}^c (r^c - 1)}{x_0 r (r - 1)} x + a - \frac{bx_0{}^c (r^c - r)}{r - 1}.$$

These two lines intersect in a point whose ordinate is a. In Fig. 13 x_0 is taken equal to 2 and r equal to 2. The value of a is found to be 2.72. The formula then becomes

$$y - 2.72 = bx^c,$$

or

$$\log (y - 2.72) = \log b + c \log x.$$

In Fig. 14 log $(y-2.72)$ is plotted to log x and b and c determined as in XII. It is seen that the points lie very nearly on a straight line. The values of c and b are read from Fig. 14.

$$c = 1.3;$$

$$\log b = 9.7840 - 10;$$

$$b = .61.$$

The law, connecting x and y then is

$$y = 2.72 + .61x^{1.3}.$$

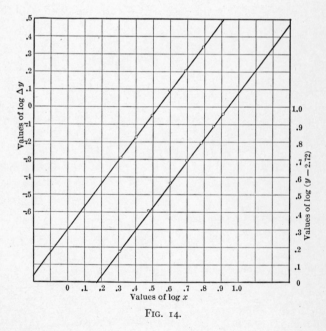

FIG. 14.

The values of y computed from this formula are written in the last line of the table.

Second Method. From the equation

$$y = a + bx^c$$

we have

$$y + \Delta y = a + bx^c r^c;$$

$$\Delta y = bx^c(r^c - 1);$$

$$\log \Delta y = \log b(r^c - 1) + c \log x.$$

This is the equation of a straight line when $\log \Delta y$ is plotted to $\log x$. Fig. 14 shows the points so plotted and from the line drawn through them the values of b and c are obtained.

$$c = 1.3,$$

$$b = .61.$$

a is found by taking the average of all the values obtained from the equation

$$a = y - .61^{1.3}.$$

a is equal to 2.72.

XV. $y = a10^{bx^c}$.

Values of x form a geometrical series and $\Delta \log y$ form a geometrical series.

If two variables, x and y, are so related that when values of x are taken in a geometrical series the first differences of the corresponding values of $\log y$ form a geometrical series, the relation between the variables is expressed by the equation

XV $\qquad\qquad y = a10^{bx^c}.$

This equation written in the logarithmic form is

$$\log y = \log a + bx^c.$$

Comparing this with XIV it is evident that if the values of x form a geometrical series the first differences of the corresponding values of $\log y$ also form a geometrical series.

In an experiment to determine the upward pressure of water seeping through sand a tank in the form shown in Fig. 15 was filled with sand of a given porosity and a constant head of water of four feet maintained.*   The water was allowed to flow freely from the tank at A.   The height of the column of water

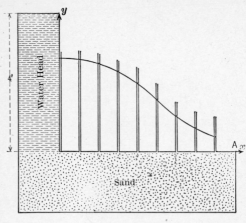

FIG. 15.

in each glass tube, six inches apart, was measured.   In the table below x represents the distance of the tube from the water head in feet, and y the height of the column of water in the tube, also in feet.   It is required to find the law connecting x and y.

Tube	1	2	3	4	5	6	7	8	9
x	0	.5	1.0	1.5	2.0	2.5	3.0	3.5	4.0
y	2.31	2.30	2.20	2.00	1.66	1.24	0.84	0.54	0.28
log y	.3636	.3617	.3424	.3010	.2201	.0934	− .0757	− .2676	− .5528
x	....	.5	1.0	......	2.0	......	......	......	4.0
y	....	2.30	2.20	......	1.66	......	......	......	.28
log y	....	.3617	.3424	......	.2201	......	......	......	− .5528
Δ log y	....	− .0193	− .1223	......	− .7729				
log x	....	− .3010	.0000	......	.3010				
log (−Δ log y)	.:..	−1.7144	− .9126	......	− .1119				
bx^c	.0000	− .0036	− .0228	− .0673	− .1449	− .2627	− .4272	− .6445	− .9201
log $(y−bx^c)$	.3636	.3653	.3652	.3683	.3650	.3561	.3515	.3769	.3673
Computed y	2.314	2.295	2.195	1.982	1.658	1.264	.865	.525	.278

In the fifth line values of x are selected in a geometrical series and the corresponding values of y written in the next line.   In Fig. 16 log $(−Δ$ log $y)$ is plotted to log x.   The points lie on a straight line.   On account of the small number of points used in the test we select formula XV on trial. From the formula

$$y = a10^{bx^c}$$

it follows that

$$\log y = \log a + bx^c$$

* Coleman's Thesis, University of Michigan.

$$\log y_k = \log a + bx_k^c$$

$$\log y_{k+1} = \log a + bx_k^c r^c$$

$$\Delta \log y_k = bx_k^c (r^c - 1)$$

$$\log (\Delta \log y) = \log b(r^c - 1) + c \log x.$$

If $\Delta \log y$ is negative b is negative, in which case it is only necessary to divide the equation by -1 before taking the logarithms of the two members of the equation.

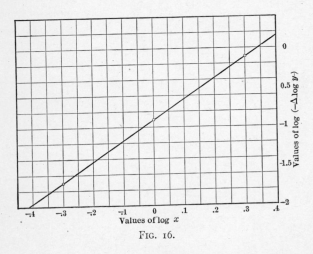

FIG. 16.

The last equation above represents a straight line when $\log (\Delta \log y)$ is plotted to $\log x$. The slope gives the value of c and the intercept gives $\log b(r^c - 1)$. From Fig. 16 values of b and c are readily obtained.

$$c = 2\tfrac{2}{3},$$

$$b = -.02282.$$

In the next to the last line the value of a is computed for each value of x from the equation

$$\log a = \log y + .0228 x^{2\frac{1}{3}}.$$

The average of these values of a gives

$$a = 2.314.$$

The formula obtained is

$$y = (2.314) \, 10^{-.0228x^{2\frac{1}{4}}}.$$

The values of y computed from this equation are written in the last line of the table. The agreement is not a bad one.

CHAPTER IV

XVI. $(x+a)(y+b)=c.$

Points represented by $\left(x-x_k, \dfrac{x-x_k}{y-y_k}\right)$ lie on a straight line.

If two variables, x and y, are so related that the points represented by $\left(x-x_k, \dfrac{x-x_k}{y-y_k}\right)$ *lie on a straight line, the relation between the variables is expressed by the equation*

XVI
$$(x+a)(y+b)=c.$$

$$\text{Let } x-x_k=X,$$

$$y-y_k=Y,$$

where x_k and y_k are any two corresponding values of x and y. From the above equations

$$x=X+x_k,$$

$$y=Y+y_k.$$

Substituting these values of x and y in equation XVI we have

$$(X+x_k+a)(Y+y_k+b)=c,$$

or

$$XY+(y_k+b)X+(x_k+a)Y+(x_k+a)(y_k+b)=c.$$

Since (x_k, y_k) is a point on the curve

$$(x_k+a)(y_k+b)=c,$$

and

$$XY+(y_k+b)X+(x_k+a)Y=0.$$

Dividing the last equation by Y

$$X+(y_k+b)\frac{X}{Y}+x_k+a=0,$$

or

$$\frac{X}{Y}=-\frac{1}{y_k+b}X-\frac{x+a}{y_k+b}.$$

This represents a straight line when X is plotted to $\frac{X}{Y}$.

The theorem is proved directly as follows: If the points $\left(x-x,\dfrac{x-x_k}{y-y_k}\right)$ lie on a straight line its equation will be

$$\frac{x-x_k}{y-y_k}=p(x-x_k)+q.$$

Clearing of fractions

$$x-x_k=p(x-x_k)(y-y_k)+q(y-y_k).$$

This is plainly of the form

$$(x+a)(y+b)=c.$$

The following tables of values is taken from Ex. 18, page 138 of Saxelby's Practical Mathematics. It represents the results of experiments to find the relation between the potential difference V and the current A in the electric arc. The length of the arc was 3 mm.

A (amperes)	1.96	2.46	2.97	3.45	3.96	4.97	5.97	6.97	7.97
V (volts)	67.00	62.75	59.75	58.50	56.00	53.50	52.00	51.40	50.60
X	0	0.50	1.01	1.49	2.00	3.01	4.01	5.01	6.01
Y	0	−4.25	−7.25	−8.50	−11.00	−13.50	−15.00	−15.60	−16.40
$\frac{X}{Y}$	...	−.1176	−.1393	−.1752	−.1817	−.2228	−.2670	−.3210	−.3665
Computed V	66.99	62.74	59.80	57.80	56.19	53.94	52.44	51.36	50.55

Let A be taken as abscissa and V as ordinate and transfer the origin to the point (1.96, 67.00) by the substitution

$$X=A-1.96,$$

$$Y=V-67.00.$$

The values of X and Y are given in the third and fourth lines of the table. The values of $\dfrac{X}{Y}$ are plotted to X in Fig. 17

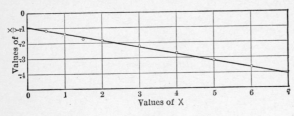

FIG. 17.

and are seen to lie nearly on a straight line. It is therefore concluded that the formula is

$$(V+b)(A+a)=c.$$

By the equations of substitution this becomes

$$(X+1.96+a)(Y+67.00+b)=c,$$

or

$$XY+(67.00+b)X+(1.96+b)Y=0.$$

Dividing by $Y(67.00+b)$

$$\frac{X}{Y}=-\frac{1}{67.00+b}X-\frac{1.96+a}{67.00+b}.$$

The slope of this line is $-\dfrac{1}{67.00+b}$ and the intercept is

$-\dfrac{1.96+a}{67.00+b}$. From Fig. 17

$$\frac{1}{67.00+b}=.045;$$

$$\frac{1.96+a}{67.00+b}=.095.$$

Solving these equations

$$a=0.151,$$
$$b=-44.78,$$

From formula

$$c=46.89.$$

These values give

$$(A+0.151)(V-44.78)=46.89.$$

In the last line of the table are written the values of V computed from the above formula

$$\text{XVI}a. \quad y=a10^{\frac{b}{x+c}}.$$

Points represented by $\left(\dfrac{1}{x-x_k}\log\dfrac{y}{y_k},\ \log\dfrac{y}{y_k}\right)$ lie on a straight line.

If two variables, x and y, are so related that the points represented by $\left(\dfrac{1}{x-x_k}\log\dfrac{y}{y_k},\ \log\dfrac{y}{y_k}\right)$ lie on a straight line, the relation between the variables is expressed by the equation

XVIa $y=a10^{\frac{b}{x+c}}.$

By the condition stated

$$\log\frac{y}{y_k}=m\ \frac{1}{x-x_k}\ \log\frac{y}{y_k}+b,$$

where x_k and y_k represent any two corresponding values of x and y. m is the slope of the line and b its intercept. Clearing the equation of fractions

$$(\log y-\log y_k)(x-x_k)=m(\log y-\log y_k)+b(x-x_k),$$

or

$$\log y(x-x_k-m)=(b+\log y_k)x-\log y_k(x_k+m)-bx_k.$$

$$\log y=\frac{(b+\log y_k)x-\log y_k(x_k+m)-bx_k}{x-x_k-m}$$

$$=\frac{Ax+B}{x+C}$$

$$=A+\frac{B-AC}{x+C}$$

$$=\log a+\frac{b}{x+c}.$$

Therefore

$$y = 10^{\log a} \; 10^{\frac{b}{x+c}}$$

$$= a 10^{\frac{b}{x+c}}.$$

For the purpose of determining the constants the equation is written in the form

$$\log y = \log a + \frac{b}{x+c},$$

$$(\log y - \log a)(x+c) = b,$$

Let

$$\log y = \log Y + \log y_k,$$

and

$$x = X + x_k.$$

Then follows

$$(\log Y + \log y_k - \log a)(X + x_k + c) = b,$$

$$X \log Y + \log Y(x_k+c) + X(\log y_k - \log a) + (\log y_k - \log a)(x_k+c) = b.$$

But

$$(\log y_k - \log a)(x_k+c) = b,$$

since the point (x_k, y_k) lies on the curve.

$$X \log Y + \log Y(x_k+c) + X(\log y_k - \log a) = 0.$$

Dividing this equation by X

$$\log Y = -(x_k+c)\frac{\log Y}{X} + \log a - \log y_k.$$

Replacing $\log Y$ and X by their values

$$\log \frac{y}{y_k} = -(x_k+c)\frac{1}{x-x_k}\log \frac{y}{y_k} + \log a - \log y_k.$$

From this it is seen that if $\log \dfrac{y}{y_k}$ be plotted to $\dfrac{1}{x-x_k}\log \dfrac{y}{y_k}$ a straight line is obtained whose slope is $-(x_k+c)$ and whose intercept is $\log a - \log y_k$. If the slope of the line is represented by M and the intercept by B

$$c = -M - x_k,$$

$$\log a = B + \log y_k.$$

By writing XVIa in the logarithmic form

$$\log y = b\,\frac{1}{x+c} + \log a$$

a line is obtained whose slope is b.

XVII. $y = ae^{cx} + be^{dx}$.

Values of x form an arithmetical series and the points $\left(\dfrac{y_{k+1}}{y_k}, \dfrac{y_{k+2}}{y_k}\right)$ lie on a straight line whose slope, M, is positive and intercept, B, is negative, and $M^2 + 4B$ positive.

If two variables, x and y, are so related that when values of x are taken in an arithmetical series the points represented by $\left(\dfrac{y_{k+1}}{y_k}, \dfrac{y_{k+2}}{y_k}\right)$ lie on a straight line whose slope, M, is positive and whose intercept, B, is negative and also $M^2 + 4B$ is positive the relation between the variables is expressed by the equation

XVII $y = ae^{cx} + be^{dx}$.

Let (x_k, y_k), $(x + \Delta x, y_{k+1})$, $(x_k + 2\Delta x, y_{k+2})$ be three sets of corresponding values of x and y where the values of x are taken in an arithmetical series.   We can then write the three equations, provided these values satisfy XVII.

$$y_k = ae^{cx_k} + be^{dx_k}, \qquad \ldots \ldots \ldots \quad (1)$$

$$y_{k+1} = ae^{cx_k}e^{c\Delta x} + be^{dx_k}e^{d\Delta x}, \qquad \ldots \ldots \quad (2)$$

$$y_{k+2} = ae^{cx_k}e^{2c\Delta x} + be^{dx_k}e^{2d\Delta x}. \qquad \ldots \ldots \quad (3)$$

Multiplying (1) by $e^{c\Delta x}$ and subtracting the resulting equation from (2)

$$y_{k+1} - e^{c\Delta x}y_k = be^{dx_k}\left(e^{d\Delta x} - e^{c\Delta x}\right). \qquad \ldots \ldots \quad (4)$$

Multiplying (2) by $e^{c\Delta x}$ and subtracting from (3)

$$y_{k+2} - e^{c\Delta x}y_{k+1} = be^{dx_k}\left(e^{2d\Delta x} - e_{(c+d)\Delta x}\right). \qquad \ldots \ldots \quad (5)$$

Multiplying (4) by $e^{d\Delta x}$ and subtracting from (5) there results

$$y_{k+2} - (e^{c\Delta x} + e^{d\Delta x})y_{k+1} + e^{(c+d)\Delta x}y_k = 0, \quad . \quad \cdot \quad . \quad (6)$$

or

$$\frac{y_{k+2}}{y_k} = (e^{c\Delta x} + e^{d\Delta x})\frac{y_{k+1}}{y_k} - e^{(c+d)\Delta x}.$$

The values of c and d are fixed for any tabulated function which can be represented by XVII, and therefore, the last equation represents a straight line when $\frac{y_{k+2}}{y_k}$ is plotted to $\frac{y_{k+1}}{y_k}$. The slope of the line is

$$M = e^{c\Delta x} + e^{d\Delta x},$$

and the intercept is

$$B = -e^{(c+d)\Delta x}.$$

It is seen that M is positive, B negative, and $M^2 + 4B$ positive, for

$$M^2 = e^{2c\Delta x} + 2e^{(c+d)\Delta x} + e^{2d\Delta x},$$

$$4B = -4e^{(c+d)\Delta x},$$

and

$$M^2 + 4B = (e^{c\Delta x} - e^{d\Delta x})^2.$$

In the first two lines of the table are given corresponding values of x and y. It is desired to find a formula which will express the relations between them.

x	1.0	1.5	2.0	2.5	3.0	3.5	4.0	4.5	5.0
y	+.3762	+.0906	−.1826	− .4463	− .7039	− .9582	−1.2119	−1.4677	−1.7280
$\frac{y_{k+1}}{y_k}$	.....	.....	+.241	−2.015	+2.444	+1.577	+1.361	+1.265	+1.211
$\frac{y_{k+2}}{y_k}$	.....	.....	−.485	−4.926	+3.855	+2.147	+1.722	+1.532	+1.426
$e^{-.412x}$	+.662	+.539	+.439	+ .359	+ .290	+ .236	+ .192	+.157	+ .127
$ye^{-.165x}$	+.319	+.071	−.131	− .295	− .429	− .538	− .626	− .698	− .757
Computed y	+.371	+.087	−.185	− .447	− .704	− .957	−1.210	−1.464	−1.723

Plotting the points represented by $\left(\dfrac{y_{k+1}}{y_k}, \dfrac{y_{k+2}}{y_k}\right)$, Fig. 18, a straight line is obtained whose equation is

$$\frac{y_{k+2}}{y_k} = 1.97\frac{y_{k+1}}{y_k} - .96,$$

$$M = 1.97,$$

$$B = - .96.$$

Since M is positive, B negative, and $M^2 + 4B$ positive, it follows that the relation between the variables is expressed approximately by XVII. It has been shown that the slope

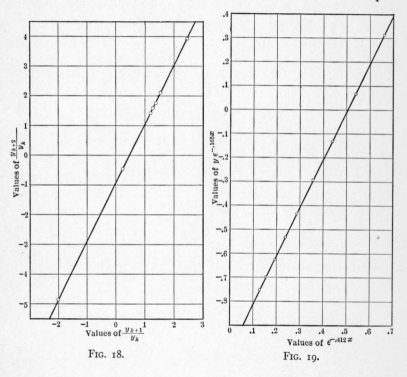

FIG. 18.   FIG. 19.

of the line is equal to $e^{c\Delta x} + e^{d\Delta x}$, and the intercept is equal to $-e^{(c+d)\Delta x}$. Since Δx is .5

$$e^{\frac{1}{2}c}e^{\frac{1}{2}d} = 1.97,$$

$$e^{\frac{1}{2}(c+d)} = .96.$$

From these equations are obtained the values of c and d,

$$c = -.247,$$

$$d = .165.$$

The formula is now

$$y = ae^{-.247x} + be^{.165x}.$$

Dividing both sides of this equation by $e^{.165x}$ gives the equation

$$ye^{-.165x} = ae^{-.412x} + b,$$

which represents a straight line when $ye^{-.165x}$ is plotted to $e^{-.412x}$. The values of these quantities taken from the table are plotted in Fig. 19 and are seen to lie very nearly on a straight line.

This line has the slope 2.00 and intercept -1.01. Substituting these values of a and b in the formula it becomes

$$y = 2e^{-.247x} - 1.01e^{.165x}.$$

It is seen that the errors in the values of y computed from this formula are in the third decimal place. The values are as good as could be expected from a formula in which the constants are determined graphically. For a better determination of the constants the method of Chapter VI must be employed.

XVIII. $y = e^{ax}(c \cos bx + d \sin bx)$.

Values of x form an arithmetical series, and the points $\left(\dfrac{y_{k+1}}{y_k}, \dfrac{y_{k+2}}{y_k}\right)$ lie on a straight line. Also $M^2 + 4B$ is negative.

If two variables, x and y, are so related that when values of x are taken in an arithmetical series the points represented by $\left(\dfrac{y_{k+1}}{y_k}, \dfrac{y_{k+2}}{y_k}\right)$ lie on a straight line whose slope M and intercept B have such values that $M^2 + 4B$ is negative, the relation between the variables is expressed by the equation

XVIII $\qquad\qquad y = e^{ax}(c \cos bx + d \sin bx)$.

Let x and y_k be any two corresponding values of the variables. We have the three equations

$$y_k = e^{ax}(c \cos bx + d \sin bx), \quad \cdots \cdots \cdots \cdots \quad (1)$$

$$y_{k+1} = e^{ax}e^{a\Delta x}[c \cos (bx + b\Delta x) + d \sin (bx + b\Delta x)]$$

$$= e^{ax}e^{a\Delta x}[c(\cos bx \cos b\Delta x - \sin bx \sin b\Delta x)$$
$$+ d(\sin bx \cos b\Delta x + \cos bx \sin b\Delta x)]$$
$$= e^{ax}e^{a\Delta x}[(c \cos b\Delta x + d \sin b\Delta x)\cos bx$$
$$+ (d \cos b\Delta x - c \sin b\Delta x)\sin bx]. \quad . \quad (2)$$

The value y_{k+2} can be written directly from the value of y_{k+1} by replacing Δx by $2\Delta x$.

$$y_{k+2} = e^{ax}e^{2a\Delta x}[(c \cos 2b\Delta x + d \sin 2b\Delta x)\cos bx$$
$$+ (d \cos 2b\Delta x - c \sin 2b\Delta x)\sin bx]. \quad . \quad . \quad . \quad (3)$$

Subtracting (1) multiplied by $e^{a\Delta x}(c \cos b\Delta x + d \sin b\Delta x)$ from (2) multiplied by c we have

$$cy_{k+1} - e^{a\Delta x}(c \cos b\Delta x + d \sin b\Delta x)y_k$$
$$= ce^{ax}e^{a\Delta x}(d \cos b\Delta x - c \sin b\Delta x)\sin bx$$
$$- de^{ax}e^{a\Delta x}(c \cos b\Delta x + d \sin b\Delta x)\sin bx$$
$$= -(c^2 + d^2)e^{ax}e^{a\Delta x} \sin b\Delta x \sin bx. \quad . \quad . \quad . \quad . \quad . \quad . \quad (4)$$

Similarly

$$cy_{k+2} - e^{2a\Delta x}(c \cos 2b\Delta x + d \sin 2b\Delta x)y_k$$
$$= -(c^2 + d^2)e^{ax}e^{2a\Delta x} \sin 2b\Delta x \sin bx. \quad . \quad . \quad . \quad (5)$$

Multiplying equation (4) by $e^{a\Delta x} \sin 2b\Delta x$ and subtracting it from (5) multiplied by $\sin b\Delta x$

$$c \sin b\Delta x y_{k+2} - e^{2a\Delta x}(c \cos 2b\Delta x \sin b\Delta x + d \sin 2b\Delta x \sin b\Delta x)y_k$$
$$- ce^{a\Delta x} \sin 2b\Delta x y_{k+1} + e^{2a\Delta x}(c \cos b\Delta x \sin 2b\Delta x$$
$$+ d \sin b\Delta x \sin 2b\Delta x)y_k = 0.$$

Simplifying

$$c \sin b\Delta x y_{k+2} - ce^{a\Delta x} \sin 2b\Delta x y_{k+1} + ce^{2a\Delta x} \sin b\Delta x y_k = 0.$$

Dividing by $c \sin b\Delta x y_k$,

$$\frac{y_{k+2}}{y_k} = 2 \cos b\Delta x e^{a\Delta x}\frac{y_{k+1}}{y_k} - e^{2a\Delta x}.$$

The values of a and b will be fixed for any tabulated function which can be represented by XVIII, and therefore, the last equation represents a straight line when $\dfrac{y_{k+2}}{y_k}$ is plotted to $\dfrac{y_{k+1}}{y_k}$. The slope of the line is

$$M = 2e^{a\Delta x} \cos b\Delta x,$$

and the intercept

$$B = -e^{2a\Delta x}.$$

It is evident that $M^2 + 4B$ is negative.

It is possible that in a special case $M^2 + 4B$ might be zero, but then b would be zero and hence

$$y = ce^{ax},$$

which is formula V.

Corresponding values of x and y are given in the first two columns of the table below. It is required to find a formula which will represent approximately the relation between them.

x	y	$\dfrac{y_{k+1}}{y_k}$	$\dfrac{y_{k+2}}{y_k}$	$e^{.08x}$	$\cos bx$	$\tan bx$	$\dfrac{e^{.08x}}{\cos bx}$	$\dfrac{y}{e^{.08x}\cos bx}$	Computed y
0	+ .300	....	.....	1.0000	1.0000	.0000	1.0000	+ .300	+ .308
1	+ .011	....	.....	1.0833	+ .8646	+ .5812	+ .9366	+ .012	+ .018
2	− .332	+ .04	− 1.11	1.1735	+ .4950	+ 1.7556	+ .5809	− .571	− .327
3	− .636	−30.2	−57.8	1.2712	− .0087	−114.59	− .0111	+57.3	− .634
4	− .803	+1.92	+ 2.42	1.3771	− .5100	1.6864	− .7023	+ 1.143	− .804
5	− .761	+1.26	+ 1.20	1.4918	− .8732	.5581	−1.3026	+ .584	− .761
6	− .485	+ .95	+ .60	1.6161	− .9998	+ .0175	−1.6159	+ .300	− .485
7	− .017	+ .64	+ .02	1.7507	− .8557	+ .6048	−1.4981	+ .011	− .012
8	+ .537	+ .04	− 1.11	1.8965	− .4797	1.8291	− .9998	− .590	+ .545
9	+1.027	−31.6	−60.4	2.0544	+ .0262	− 38.1880	+ .0538	+19.08	+1.035
10	+1.298	+1.91	+ 2.42	2.2255	+ .5250	1.6212	+1.1684	+1 .111	+1.299

In Fig. 20 the points represented by $\left(\dfrac{y_{k+1}}{y_k}, \dfrac{y_{k+2}}{y_k}\right)$ are plotted. They lie very nearly on the straight line whose equation is

$$\frac{y_{k+2}}{y_k} = 1.875\, \frac{y_{k+1}}{y_k} - 1.175.$$

Since $(1.878)^2 - 4(1.18)$ is negative the relation between the variables is expressed approximately by the equation

$$y = e^{ax}(c \cos bx + d \sin bx).$$

It was shown that the slope of the line is equal to $2(\cos b\Delta x)e^{a\Delta x}$ and the intercept equal to $-e^{2a\Delta x}$. Since Δx is equal to unity we have

$$2e^a \cos b = 1.875,$$

$$e^{2a} = 1.175,$$

$$\log \cos b = 9.9370 - 10,$$

$$b = 30° \, 10' \text{ ap-proximately,}$$

$$a = .08.$$

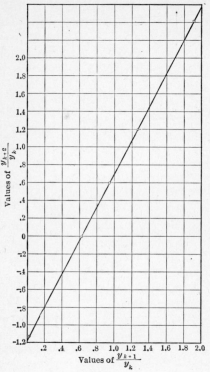

Values of $\dfrac{y_{k+2}}{y_k}$

Values of $\dfrac{y_{k+1}}{y_k}$

FIG. 20.

The formula is now

$$y = e^{.08x}(c \cos 30\tfrac{1}{6}x + d \sin 30\tfrac{1}{6}x),$$

where $30\tfrac{1}{6}$ is expressed in degrees.

Dividing the equation by $e^{.08x} \cos 30\tfrac{1}{6}x$

$$\frac{y}{e^{.08x} \cos 30\tfrac{1}{6}x°} = c + d \tan 30\tfrac{1}{6}x°,$$

which is a straight line when $\dfrac{y}{e^{.08x} \cos 30\tfrac{1}{6}x°}$ is plotted to $\tan 30\tfrac{1}{6}x°$. In Fig. 21 these points are plotted and are seen to lie nearly on a straight line whose slope is $-.496$ and intercept

.308. Two of the points are omitted in the figure on account of the magnitude of the coördinates. Substituting the values of constants just found in the formula the equation expressing the relation between x and y is

$$y = e^{.08x}(.308 \cos 30\tfrac{1}{6}x° - .496 \sin 30\tfrac{1}{6}x°).$$

The last column in the table gives the values of y computed from the equation. The agreement with the original values is fairly good.

In case c is zero XVIII becomes the equation for damped vibrations, $y = de^{ax} \sin bx$.

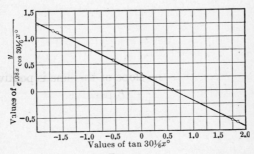

FIG. 21.

XIX. $y = ax^c_{\,\,} + bx^d$.

Values of x form a geometrical series, and the points $\left(\dfrac{y_{k+1}}{y_k}, \dfrac{y_{k+2}}{y_k}\right)$ lie on a straight line, whose slope, M, is positive, and whose intercept, B, is negative, and $M^2 + 4B$ positive.

If two variables, x and y, are so related that when values of x are taken in a geometrical series the points represented by $\left(\dfrac{y_{k+1}}{y_k}, \dfrac{y_{k+2}}{y_k}\right)$ lie on a straight line whose slope, M, is positive, and intercept, B, negative, and also $M^2 + 4B$ positive, the relation between the variables is expressed by the equation

XIX $\qquad\qquad y = ax^c + bx^d.$

Let x and y_k be any two corresponding values of the variables. The following equations are evident:

$$y_k = ax^c + bx^d, \quad \cdots \cdots \quad (1)$$

$$y_{k+1} = ax^c r^c + bx^d r^d, \quad \cdots \cdots \quad (2)$$

$$y_{k+2} = ax^c r^{2c} + bx^d r^{2d}, \quad \ldots \quad (3)$$

$$y_{k+1} - r^c y_k = bx^d(r^d - r^c), \quad \ldots \quad (4)$$

$$y_{k+2} - r^c y_{k+1} = bx^d r^d(r^d - r^c). \quad \ldots \quad (5)$$

Multiplying equation (4) by γ^d and subtracting it from equation (5) there results

$$y_{k+2} - r^c y_{k+1} - r^d y_{k+1} + r^{c+d} y_k = 0,$$

or

$$\frac{y_{k+2}}{y_k} = (r^c + r^d)\frac{y_{k+1}}{y_k} - r^{c+d}.$$

It is seen that the slope of this line is positive and the intercept negative, and $M^2 + 4B$ positive.

In the table* below, the values of x and y from $x = .05$ to $x = .55$ are taken from Peddle's Construction of Graphical Charts.

x	y	x	y	$\dfrac{y_{k+1}}{y_k}$	$\dfrac{y_{k+2}}{y_k}$	$x^{.55}$	$x^{.85}$	$\dfrac{y}{x^{.55}}$	Computed y
.05	.283	.05	.283	....	....	.192	.078	1.470	.283
.10	.402	.10	.402	....	....	.282	.141	1.426	.402
.15	.488	...	....	....	....	.352	.199	1.385	.488
.20	.556	.20	.556	1.420	1.965	.413	.255	1.347	.556
.25	.613	...	....	....	....	.466	.308	1.315	.612
.30	.658	...	....	....	....	.516	.359	1.276	.658
.35	.695	...	....	....	....	.561	.410	1.238	.697
.40	.730	.40	.730	1.383	1.816	.609	.459	1.208	.730
.45	.757	...	....	....	....	.645	.507	1.174	.757
.50	.780	...	....	....	....	.683	.555	1.142	.780
.55	.800	...	....	....	....	.720	.602	1.114	.799
.60	.814	...	....	....	....	.755	.648	1.078	.814
.65	.826	...	....	....	....	.789	.693	1.047	.826
.70	.835	...	....	....	....	.822	.738	1.016	.835
.75	.840	...	....	....	....	.854	.783	0.984	.840
.80	.845	.80	.845	1.313	1.520	.885	.829	0.955	.846

In column 3 the values of x are selected in geometrical ratio and the corresponding values of y are given in column 4. The points $\left(\dfrac{y_{k+1}}{y_k}, \dfrac{y_{k+2}}{y_k}\right)$ are plotted in Fig. 22, and although the

* See Rateau's "Flow of Steam Through Nozzles."

three points do not lie exactly on a straight line the approximation is good. The slope of the line is 4.10 and the intercept
−3.86 which give the equations

$$2^c + 2^d = 4.10,$$

$$2^{c+d} = 3.86.$$

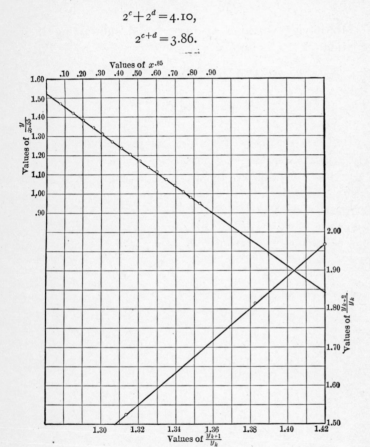

FIG. 22 AND FIG. 23.

Solving these equations the values of c and d are found to be

$$e = 1.40,$$

$$d = .55.$$

The formula now is

$$y = ax^{1.4} + bx^{.55}.$$

Dividing both members of this equation by $x^{.55}$

$$\frac{y}{x^{.55}} = ax^{.85} + b,$$

which represents a straight line when $\frac{y}{x^{.55}}$ is plotted to $x^{.85}$.
The slope of the line is equal to a and the intercept equal to b.
From Fig. 23

$$a = - .685,$$

$$b = 1.522.$$

The formula after the constants have been replaced by their numerical values is

$$y = 1.522x^{.55} - .685x^{1.40}.$$

The last column of the table shows that the fit is quite good.

If the errors of observation are so small that the values of the dependent variable can be relied on to the last figure derivatives may be made use of to advantage in evaluating the constants in empirical formulas. But when the values can not be so relied on, or when the data must first be leveled graphically or otherwise, the employment of derivatives may lead to very erroneous results. This will be illustrated by two examples worked out in detail.

The first step in the process is to write the differential equation of the formula used and then from this equation find the values of the constants.

Consider the formula

$$y = e^{ax}(c \cos bx + d \sin bx).$$

Looking upon a and b as known constants and c and d as constants of integration, the corresponding differential equation is

$$y'' - 2ay' + (a^2 + b^2)y = 0.$$

Dividing this equation by y

$$\frac{y''}{y} = 2a\frac{y'}{y} - (a^2 + b^2),$$

which, if the data can be represented by XVIII, represents a straight line whose slope is $2a$ and whose intercept is $-(a^2+b^2)$. Corresponding values of x and y are given in the table.

x	y	y'	y''	$\dfrac{y'}{y}$	$\dfrac{y''}{y}$	x De-grees	x Min-utes	$e^{.06x}$	cos .08x	tan .08x	$\dfrac{y}{e^{.06x}\cos .08x}$
0	+ .3000	.....	.....	......	.....	0	0	1.0000	1.0000	.0000	+ .3000
1	+ .2750	.....		......	.....	4	35.02	1.0618	.9968	.0802	+ .2598
2	+ .2441	− .0342	− .0068	− .1401	− .0279	9	10.04	1.1275	.9872	.1614	+ .2193
3	+ .2065	− .0429	− .0066	− .1976	− .0319	13	45.06	1.1972	.9713	.2447	+ .1776
4	+ .1622	− .0481	− .0078	− .2965	− .0481	18	20.08	1.2712	.9492	.3314	+ .1344
5	+ .1102	− .0557	− .0075	− .5054	− .0681	22	55.10	1.3499	.9211	.4228	+ .0886
6	+ .0506	− .0635	− .0086	− 1.2549	− .1700	27	30.12	1.4333	.8870	.5206	+ .0398
7	− .0175	− .0721	− .0080	+ 4.1200	+ .4571	32	05.14	1.5220	.8472	.6270	− .0136
8	− .0937	− .0805	− .0087	+ .8591	+ .0928	36	40.16	1.6161	.8021	.7446	− .0723
9	− .1786	− .0894	− .0091	+ .5011	+ .0510	41	15.18	1.7160	.7519	.8771	− .1384
10	− .2726	− .0985	− .0091	+ .3247	+ .0334	45	50.20	1.8221	.6967	1.0296	− .2147
11	− .3757	− .1078	− .0085	+ .2869	+ .0226	50	25.22	1.9348	.6372	1.2097	− .3047
12	− .4881	− .1168	− .0087	+ .2393	+ .0178	55	00.24	2.0544	.5735	1.4284	− .4143
13	− .6093	− .1257	− .0091	+ .2063	+ .0149	59	35.26	2.1815	.5062	1.7036	− .5518
14	− .7396	− .1348	− .0089	+ .1823	+ .0120	64	10.28	2.3164	.4357	2.0659	− .7328
15	− .8788	− .1435	− .0084	+ .1633	+ .0096	68	45.30	2.4596	.3624	2.5722	− .9859
16	−1.0264	.....	.....	......	.....	73	20.32	2.6117	.2867	3.3414	−1.3707
17	−1.1814	.....	.....	......	.....	77	55.34	2.7732	.2098	4.6735	−2.0306

The values of y' and y'' are obtained by the formulas

$$y'_n = \frac{1}{12h}\ (y_{n-2} - 8y_{n-1} + 8y_{n+1} - y_{n+2}),$$

$$y''_n = -\frac{1}{12h^2}\ (y_{n-2} - 16y_{n-1} + 30y_n - 16y_{n+1} + y_{n+2}),$$

where $h = \Delta x = 1$. These formulas are derived in Chapter VI.

Plotting the points represented by $\left(\dfrac{y'}{y}, \dfrac{y''}{y}\right)$, Fig. 24, it is seen that they lie nearly on a straight line whose slope is .12 and intercept −.01. Therefore

$$2a = .12,$$

$$a^2 + b^2 = .01,$$

$$a = .06,$$

$$b = .08.$$

We have then

$$y = e^{.06x}(c \cos .08x + d \sin .08x).$$

Dividing this equation by $e^{.06x}$ cos .08x

$$\frac{y}{e^{.06x} \cos .08x} = c + d \tan .08x.$$

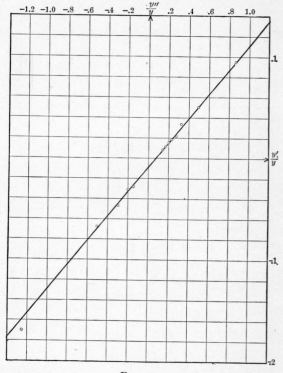

FIG. 24.

This represents a straight line when $\dfrac{y}{e^{.06x} \cos .08x}$ is plotted to tan .08x. The slope is d and intercept c. From Fig. 25

$$d = -.5,$$

$$c = \quad .3.$$

The law connecting the variables is represented by

$$y = e^{.06x}(.3 \cos .08x - .5 \sin .08x).$$

The values of y computed from this formula agree with those given in the second column of the table.

Consider formula **XIX**

$$y = ax^c + bx^d.$$

The corresponding differential equation is

$$\frac{x^2 y''}{y} = (c+d-1)\frac{xy'}{y} - cd,$$

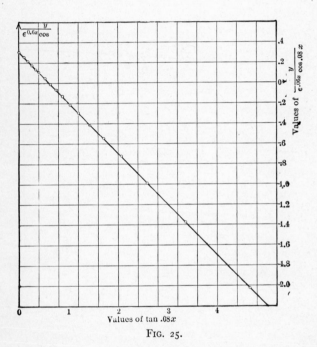

FIG. 25.

where c and d are known constants and a and b constants of integration. The differential equation represents a straight line when $\dfrac{x^2 y''}{x}$ is plotted to $\dfrac{xy'}{y}$. The slope is $c+d-1$ and the intercept is $-cd$.

The values of x and y in the table below are the same as those given in the discussion of **XIX**.

x	y	y'	y''	$\dfrac{xy'}{y}$	$\dfrac{x^2y''}{y}$
.05	.283				
.10	.402				
.15	.488	1.503	−6.933	.462	−.320
.20	.556	1.240	−4.133	.446	−.297
.25	.613	1.015	−4.967	.414	−.506
.30	.658	0.803	−3.267	.366	−.447
.35	.695	0.720	−0.400	.363	−.071
.40	.730	0.623	−3.533	.341	−.774
.45	.757	0.492	−1.500	.292	−.401
.50	.780	0.433	−1.067	.277	−.342
.55	.800	0.338	−2.633	.232	−.996
.60	.814	0.255	−0.633	.188	−.280
.65	.826	0.213	−1.200	.167	−.614
.70	.835	0.135	−1.767	.113	−1.037
.75	.840				
.80	.845				

The values of y' and y'' were computed by means of the formulas used in the preceding table. In Fig. 26 the points $\left(\dfrac{xy'}{y}, \dfrac{x^2y''}{y}\right)$ are plotted and, as is seen, the points do not determine a line. It is clear that the constants can not be determined by this method.

XIXa. $y = ax^b c^x$.

Points represented by $\left(x_n, \log \dfrac{y_{n+1}}{y_n}\right)$ lie on a straight line.

If two variables, x and y, are so related that when values of x are taken in a geometrical series the corresponding values of y are such that the points represented by $\left(x_n, \log \dfrac{y_{n+1}}{y_n}\right)$ lie on a straight line, the relation between the variables is expressed by the equation

XIXa $y = ax^b c^x$.

Using logarithms:

$$\log y_n = \log a + b \log x_n + x_n \log c,$$
$$\log y_{n+1} = \log a + b \log x_n + rx_n \log c + b \log r.$$

Subtracting the first equation from the second

$$\log \frac{y_{n+1}}{y_n} = (r-1)x_n \log c + b \log r.$$

By plotting $\log \frac{y_{n+1}}{y_n}$ to x_n a line is obtained whose slope is

$(r-1)\log c$, and since r is known c can be determined.

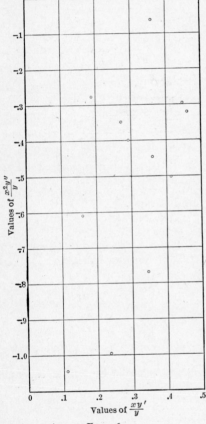

FIG. 26.

From the first equation

$$\log y_n - x_n \log c = b \log x_n + \log a.$$

If then $\log y_n - x_n \log c$ be plotted to $\log x_n$ a line is obtained whose slope is b and whose intercept is $\log a$.

CHAPTER V

XX. $y = a_0 + a_1 \cos x + a_2 \cos 2x + a_3 \cos 3x + \ldots + a_r \cos rx$
$+ b_1 \sin x + b_2 \sin 2x + b_3 \sin 3x + \ldots + b_{r-1} \sin (r-1)x.$
Values of y periodic.

The right-hand member of **XX** is called a Fourier Series when the number of terms is infinite. In the application of the formula the practical problem is to obtain a Fourier Series, of a limited number of terms, which will represent to a sufficiently close approximation a given set of data. The values of y are given as the ordinates on a curve or the ordinates of isolated points.

In what follows it is assumed that the values of y are periodic and that the period is known.

We will determine the constants in the equation

$$y = a_0 + a_1 \cos x + a_2 \cos 2x + a_3 \cos 3x, + b_1 \sin x + b_2 \sin 2x,$$

so that the curve represented by it passes through the points given by the values in the table.

x	$0°$	$60°$	$120°$	$180°$	$240°$	$300°$	$360°$
y	1.0	1.7	2.0	1.8	1.5	0.9	1.0

Substituting these values in the equation we have the following six linear relations from which the values of the six constants can be determined:

$$1.0 = a_0 + a_1 + a_2 + a_3,$$

$$1.7 = a_0 + \tfrac{1}{2}a_1 - \tfrac{1}{2}a_2 - a_3 + \frac{\sqrt{3}}{2}b_1 + \frac{\sqrt{3}}{2}b_2,$$

$$2.0 = a_0 - \tfrac{1}{2}a_1 - \tfrac{1}{2}a_2 + a_3 + \frac{\sqrt{3}}{2}b_1 - \frac{\sqrt{3}}{2}b_2,$$

$$1.8 = a_0 - a_1 + a_2 - a_3,$$

$$1.5 = a_0 - \tfrac{1}{2}a_1 - \tfrac{1}{2}a_2 + a_3 - \frac{\sqrt{3}}{2}b_1 + \frac{\sqrt{3}}{2}b_2,$$

$$0.9 = a_0 + \tfrac{1}{2}a_1 - \tfrac{1}{2}a_2 - a_3 - \frac{\sqrt{3}}{2}b_1 - \frac{\sqrt{3}}{2}b_2.$$

Multiplying each of the above equations by the coefficient of a_0 (in this case unity) in that equation and adding the resulting equations we obtain (1) below. Multiplying each equation by the coefficient of a_1 in that equation and adding we obtain (2). Proceeding in this manner with each of the constants a new set of six equations is obtained.

$$6a_0 = 8.9. \quad \cdots \cdots \cdots \quad (1)$$

$$3a_1 = -1.25. \quad \cdots \cdots \cdots \quad (2)$$

$$3a_2 = -.25. \quad \cdots \cdots \cdots \quad (3)$$

$$6a_3 = .10. \quad \cdots \cdots \cdots \quad (4)$$

$$3b_1 = .65\sqrt{3}. \quad \cdots \cdots \cdots \quad (5)$$

$$3b_2 = .15\sqrt{3}. \quad \cdots \cdots \cdots \quad (6)$$

$$a_0 = \tfrac{89}{60}, \qquad a_1 = -\tfrac{5}{12}, \qquad a_2 = -\tfrac{1}{12}, \qquad a_3 = \tfrac{1}{60},$$

$$b_1 = \tfrac{13}{60}\sqrt{3}, \qquad b_2 = \tfrac{1}{20}\sqrt{3}.$$

The equation sought is

$$y = \tfrac{89}{60} - \tfrac{5}{12}\cos x - \tfrac{1}{12}\cos 2x + \tfrac{1}{60}\cos 3x + \tfrac{13}{60}\sqrt{3}\sin x + \tfrac{1}{20}\sqrt{3}\sin 2x.$$

It reproduces exactly each one of the six given values.

The solution of a large number of equations becomes tedious and the probability of error is great. It is, therefore, very desirable to have a short and convenient method for computing the numerical values of the coefficients.*

* The scheme here used is based upon the 12-ordinate scheme of Runge. For a fuller discussion see "A Course in Fourier's Analysis and Periodogram Analysis" by Carse and Shearer.

Take the table of six sets of values

x	$0°$	$60°$	$120°$	$180°$	$240°$	$300°$
y	y_0	y_1	y_2	y_3	y_4	y_5

where the period is 2π.

For the determination of the coefficients the following six equations are obtained:

$$y_0 = a_0 + a_1 + a_2 + a_3,$$

$$y_1 = a_0 + \tfrac{1}{2}a_1 - \tfrac{1}{2}a_2 - a_3 + \frac{\sqrt{3}}{2}b_1 + \frac{\sqrt{3}}{2}b_2,$$

$$y_2 = a_0 - \tfrac{1}{2}a_1 - \tfrac{1}{2}a_2 + a_3 + \frac{\sqrt{3}}{2}b_1 - \frac{\sqrt{3}}{2}b_2,$$

$$y_3 = a_0 - a_1 + a_2 - a_3,$$

$$y_4 = a_0 - \tfrac{1}{2}a_1 - \tfrac{1}{2}a_2 + a_3 - \frac{\sqrt{3}}{2}b_1 + \frac{\sqrt{3}}{2}b_2,$$

$$y_5 = a_0 + \tfrac{1}{2}a_1 - \tfrac{1}{2}a_2 - a_3 - \frac{\sqrt{3}}{2}b_1 - \frac{\sqrt{3}}{2}b_2.$$

Proceeding in the same way as was done with numerical equations the following relations are obtained:

$$\left.\begin{aligned}
6a_0 &= y_0 + y_1 + y_2 + y_3 + y_4 + y_5,\\
3a_1 &= y_0 + \tfrac{1}{2}y_1 - \tfrac{1}{2}y_2 - y_3 - \tfrac{1}{2}y_4 + \tfrac{1}{2}y_5,\\
3a_2 &= y_0 - \tfrac{1}{2}y_1 - \tfrac{1}{2}y_2 + y_3 - \tfrac{1}{2}y_4 - \tfrac{1}{2}y_5,\\
6a_3 &= y_0 - y_1 + y_2 - y_3 + y_4 - y_5,\\
3b_1 &= +\frac{\sqrt{3}}{2}y_1 + \frac{\sqrt{3}}{2}y_2 - \frac{\sqrt{3}}{2}y_4 - \frac{\sqrt{3}}{2}y_5,\\
3b_2 &= +\frac{\sqrt{3}}{2}y_1 - \frac{\sqrt{3}}{2}y_2 + \frac{\sqrt{3}}{2}y_4 - \frac{\sqrt{3}}{2}y_5.
\end{aligned}\right\} \quad (a)$$

For convenience in computation the values of y are arranged according to the following scheme:

	y_0	y_1	y_2
	y_3	y_4	y_5
Sum	v_0	v_1	v_2
Difference	w_0	w_1	w_2

	v_0	v_1		w_0	w_1
		v_2			w_2
Sum	p_0	p_1	Sum	r_0	r_1
Difference		q_1	Difference		s_1

$$6a_0 = p_0 + p_1,$$
$$3a_1 = r_0 + \tfrac{1}{2}s_1,$$
$$3a_2 = p_0 - \tfrac{1}{2}p_1,$$
$$6a_3 = r_0 - s_1,$$
$$3b_1 = \frac{\sqrt{3}}{2}r_1,$$
$$3b_2 = \frac{\sqrt{3}}{2}q_1.$$

$$\left. \right\} \quad \cdots \cdots \cdots \quad (b)$$

It is evident that the equations in set (b) are the same as those in set (a).

For the numerical example the arrangement would be as follows:

		1.0	1.7	2.0		
		1.8	1.5	0.9		
	v_0	2.8	3.2	2.9		
	w_0	−.8	.2	1.1		
	2.8	3.2			−.8	.2
		2.9				1.1
p_0	2.8	6.1		r_0	−.8	1.3
q_1		.3		s_1		−.9

$$6a_0 = +8.90,$$
$$3a_1 = -1.25,$$
$$3a_2 = -\ .25,$$
$$6a_3 = +\ .10,$$
$$3b_1 = +\ .65\sqrt{3},$$
$$3b_2 = +\ .15\sqrt{3}.$$

It is seen that the computation is made comparatively simple. The values of the v's are indicated by v_0, the first one. The values of the p's, etc., are indicated in the same way.

8-ORDINATE SCHEME. The formula for eight ordinates which lends itself to easy computation is

$$y = a_0 + a_1 \cos\theta + a_2 \cos 2\theta + a_3 \cos 3\theta + a_4 \cos 4\theta$$
$$+ b_1 \sin\theta + b_2 \sin 2\theta + b_3 \sin 3\theta.$$

For determining the values of the constants eight equations are written from the table:

θ	0	45°	90°	135°	180°	225°	270°	315°
y	y_0	y_1	y_2	y_3	y_4	y_5	y_6	y_7

$$y_0 = a_0 + a_1 + a_2 + a_3 + a_4,$$

$$y_1 = a_0 + \frac{\sqrt{2}}{2}a_1 \quad -\frac{\sqrt{2}}{2}a_3 - a_4 + \frac{\sqrt{2}}{2}b_1 + b_2 + \frac{\sqrt{2}}{2}b_3,$$

$$y_2 = a_0 \quad -a_2 \quad +a_4 + b_1 \quad - b_3,$$

$$y_3 = a_0 - \frac{\sqrt{2}}{2}a_1 \quad +\frac{\sqrt{2}}{2}a_3 - a_4 + \frac{\sqrt{2}}{2}b_1 - b_2 + \frac{\sqrt{2}}{2}2b_3,$$

$$y_4 = a_0 - a_1 + a_2 - a_3 + a_4,$$

$$y_5 = a_0 - \frac{\sqrt{2}}{2}a_1 \quad +\frac{\sqrt{2}}{2}a_3 - a_4 - \frac{\sqrt{2}}{2}b_1 + b_2 - \frac{\sqrt{2}}{2}b_3,$$

$$y_6 = a_0 \quad -a_2 \quad +a_4 - b_1 \quad + b_3,$$

$$y_7 = a_0 + \frac{\sqrt{2}}{2}a_1 \quad -\frac{\sqrt{2}}{2}a_3 - a_4 - \frac{\sqrt{2}}{2}b_1 - b_2 - \frac{\sqrt{2}}{2}b_3.$$

From which are obtained the following eight equations:

$$8a_0 = y_0 + y_1 + y_2 + y_3 + y_4 + y_5 + y_6 + y_7,$$

$$4a_1 = y_0 + \frac{\sqrt{2}}{2}y_1 \quad -\frac{\sqrt{2}}{2}y_3 - y_4 - \frac{\sqrt{2}}{2}y_5 \quad +\frac{\sqrt{2}}{2}y_7,$$

$$4a_2 = y_0 \quad -y_2 \quad +y_4 \quad -y_6,$$

$$4a_3 = y_0 - \frac{\sqrt{2}}{2}y_1 \quad +\frac{\sqrt{2}}{2}y_3 - y_4 + \frac{\sqrt{2}}{2}y_5 \quad -\frac{\sqrt{2}}{2}y_7,$$

$$8a_4 = y_0 - \quad y_1 + y_2 - \quad y_3 + y_4 - \quad y_5 + y_6 - \quad y_7,$$

$$4b_1 = \quad \frac{\sqrt{2}}{2}y_1 + y_2 + \frac{\sqrt{2}}{2}y_3 \quad - \frac{\sqrt{2}}{2}y_5 - y_6 - \frac{\sqrt{2}}{2}y_7,$$

$$4b_2 = \quad y_1 \quad - \quad y_3 \quad + \quad y_5 \quad - \quad y_7,$$

$$4b_3 = \quad \frac{\sqrt{2}}{2}y_1 - y_2 + \frac{\sqrt{2}}{2}y_3 \quad - \frac{\sqrt{2}}{2}y_5 + y_6 - \frac{\sqrt{2}}{2}y_7.$$

For the purpose of computation the values of y will be arranged as follows:

	y_0	y_1	y_2	y_3
	y_4	y_5	y_6	y_7
Sum	v_0	v_1	v_2	v_3
Difference	w_0	w_1	w_2	w_3

	v_0	v_1		w_0	w_1	w_2
	v_2	v_3			w_3	
Sum	p_0	p_1	Sum	r_0	r_1	r_2
Difference	q_0	q_1	Difference		s_1	

$$8a_0 = p_0 + \quad p_1,$$

$$4a_1 = r_0 + \frac{\sqrt{2}}{2}s_1,$$

$$4a_2 = q_0,$$

$$4a_3 = r_0 - \frac{\sqrt{2}}{2}s_1,$$

$$8a_4 = p_0 - p_1,$$

$$4b_1 = r_2 + \frac{\sqrt{2}}{2}r_1,$$

$$4b_2 = q_1,$$

$$4b_3 = -r_2 + \frac{\sqrt{2}}{2}r_1.$$

The process will be made clear by an example:

θ	0	45°	90°	135°	180°	225°	270°	315°	360°
y	4	-2	-1	2	3	3	-1	2	4

For computation the arrangement is as follows:

$$
\begin{array}{ccccccc}
 & & 4 & -2 & -1 & 2 & \\
 & & 3 & 3 & -1 & 2 & \\
 & v_0 & 7 & 1 & -2 & 4 & \\
 & w_0 & 1 & -5 & 0 & 0 & \\
 & & & & & & \\
 & 7 & 1 & & 1 & -5 & 0 \\
 & -2 & 4 & & & 0 & \\
p_0 & 5 & 5 & r_0 & 1 & -5 & 0 \\
q_0 & 9 & -3 & s_1 & & -5 & \\
\end{array}
$$

$$8a_0 = 10,$$

$$4a_1 = 1 - \tfrac{5}{2}\sqrt{2},$$

$$4a_2 = 9,$$

$$4a_3 = 1 + \tfrac{5}{2}\sqrt{2},$$

$$8a_4 = 0,$$

$$4b_1 = -\tfrac{5}{2}\sqrt{2},$$

$$4b_2 = -3,$$

$$4b_3 = -\tfrac{5}{2}\sqrt{2}.$$

The formula becomes

$$y = 1.25 - .634 \cos\theta + 2.25 \cos 2\theta + 1.134 \cos 3\theta$$
$$- .884 \sin\theta - .75 \sin 2\theta - .884 \sin 3\theta.$$

10-ORDINATE SCHEME

	y_0	y_1	y_2	y_3	y_4	
	y_9	y_8	y_7	y_6	y_5	
Sum	v_0	v_1	v_2	v_3	v_4	v_5
Difference		w_1	w_2	w_3	w_4	

	v_0	v_1	v_2		w_1	w_2
	v_5	v_4	v_3		w_4	w_3
Sum	p_0	p_1	p_2	Sum	l_1	l_2
Difference	q_0	q_1	q_2	Difference	m_1	m_2

$$10a_0 = p_0 + p_1 + p_2,$$
$$5a_1 = q_0 + C_1 q_1 + C_2 q_2,$$
$$5a_2 = p_0 + C_2 p_1 - C_1 p_2,$$
$$5a_3 = q_0 - C_2 q_1 - C_1 q_2,$$
$$5a_4 = p_0 - C_1 p_1 + C_2 p_2,$$
$$10a_5 = q_0 - q_1 + q_2,$$
$$5b_1 = S_1 l_1 + S_2 l_2,$$
$$5b_2 = S_2 m_1 + S_1 m_2,$$
$$5b_3 = S_2 l_1 - S_1 l_2,$$
$$5b_4 = S_1 m_1 - S_2 m_2.$$

In the above equations

$$C_1 = \cos 36°, \qquad S_1 = \sin 36°,$$
$$C_2 = \cos 72°, \qquad S_2 = \sin 72°.$$

In the schemes that follow, as in the 10-ordinate one, only the results will be given.

12-Ordinate Scheme

	y_0	y_1	y_2	y_3	y_4	y_5	y_6
		y_{11}	y_{10}	y_9	y_8	y_7	
Sum	v_0	v_1	v_2	v_3	v_4	v_5	v_6
Difference		w_1	w_2	w_3	w_4	w_5	

	v_0	v_1	v_2	v_3		w_1	w_2	w_3
	v_6	v_5	v_4			w_5	w_4	
Sum	p_0	p_1	p_2	p_3	Sum	r_1	r_2	r_3
Difference	q_0	q_1	q_2		Difference	s_1	s_2	

	p_0	p_1		r_1	q_0
	p_2	p_3		r_3	q_2
Sum	l_0	l_1	Difference	t_1	t_2

$$12a_0 = l_0 + l_1,$$

$$6a_1 = q_0 + \frac{\sqrt{3}}{2}q_1 + \tfrac{1}{2}q_2,$$

$$6a_2 = p_0 - p_3 + \tfrac{1}{2}(p_1 - p_2),$$

$$6a_3 = t_2,$$

$$6a_4 = p_0 + p_3 - \tfrac{1}{2}(p_1 + p_2),$$

$$6a_5 = q_0 - \frac{\sqrt{3}}{2}q_1 + \tfrac{1}{2}q_2,$$

$$12a_6 = l_0 - l_1,$$

$$6b_1 = \tfrac{1}{2}r_1 + \frac{\sqrt{3}}{2}r_2 + r_3,$$

$$6b_2 = \frac{\sqrt{3}}{2}(s_1 + s_2),$$

$$6b_3 = t_1,$$

$$6b_4 = \frac{\sqrt{3}}{2}(s_1 - s_2),$$

$$6b_5 = \tfrac{1}{2}r_1 - \frac{\sqrt{3}}{2}r_2 + r_3.$$

16-Ordinate Scheme

	y_0	y_1	y_2	y_3	y_4	y_5	y_6	y_7	y_8
		y_{15}	y_{14}	y_{13}	y_{12}	y_{11}	y_{10}	y_9	
Sum	v_0	v_1	v_2	v_3	v_4	v_5	v_6	v_7	v_8
Difference		w_1	w_2	w_3	w_4	w_5	w_6	w_7	

		v_0	v_1	v_2	v_3	v_4
		v_8	v_7	v_6	v_5	
Sum		p_0	p_1	p_2	p_3	p_4
Difference		q_0	q_1	q_2	q_3	

	w_1	w_2	w_3	w_4
	w_7	w_6	w_5	
Sum	r_1	r_2	r_3	r_4
Difference	s_1	s_2	s_3	

	p_0	p_1	p_2			l_0	l_1
	p_4	p_3				l_2	
Sum	l_0	l_1	l_2	Sum		t_0	t_1
Difference	m_0	m_1		Difference		x_0	

$$16a_0 = t_0 + t_1,$$

$$8a_1 = q_0 + \frac{\sqrt{2}}{2}q_2 + C_1q_1 + C_2q_3,$$

$$8a_2 = m_0 + \frac{\sqrt{2}}{2}m_1,$$

$$8a_3 = q_0 - \frac{\sqrt{2}}{2}q_2 - C_1q_3 + C_2q_1,$$

$$8a_4 = x_0,$$

$$8a_5 = q_0 - \frac{\sqrt{2}}{2}q_2 + C_1q_3 - C_2q_1,$$

$$8a_6 = m_0 - \frac{\sqrt{2}}{2}m_1,$$

$$8a_7 = q_0 + \frac{\sqrt{2}}{2}q_2 - C_1q_1 - C_2q_3,$$

$$16a_8 = t_0 - t_1,$$

$$8b_1 = r_4 + \frac{\sqrt{2}}{2}r_2 + C_1r_3 + C_2r_1,$$

$$8b_2 = s_2 + \frac{\sqrt{2}}{2}(s_1 + s_3),$$

$$8b_3 = -r_4 + \frac{\sqrt{2}}{2}r_2 + C_1r_1 - C_2r_3,$$

$$8b_4 = s_1 - s_3,$$

$$8b_5 = r_4 - \frac{\sqrt{2}}{2}r_2 + C_1r_1 - C_2r_3,$$

$$8b_6 = -s_2 + \frac{\sqrt{2}}{2}(s_1 + s_3),$$

$$8b_7 = -r_4 - \frac{\sqrt{2}}{2}r_2 + C_1r_3 + C_2r_1.$$

$$C_1 = \cos 22\tfrac{1}{2}° = \sin 67\tfrac{1}{2}°,$$

$$C_2 = \sin 22\tfrac{1}{2}° = \cos 67\tfrac{1}{2}°.$$

20-Ordinate Scheme

	y_0	y_1	y_2	y_3	y_4	y_5	y_6	y_7	y_8	y_9	y_{10}
		y_{19}	y_{18}	y_{17}	y_{16}	y_{15}	y_{14}	y_{13}	y_{12}	y_{11}	
Sum	v_0	v_1	v_2	v_3	v_4	v_5	v_6	v_7	v_8	v_9	v_{10}
Difference		w_1	w_2	w_3	w_4	w_5	w_6	w_7	w_8	w_9	

	v_0	v_1	v_2	v_3	v_4	v_5
	v_{10}	v_9	v_8	v_7	v_6	
Sum	p_0	p_1	p_2	p_3	p_4	p_5
Difference	q_0	q_1	q_2	q_3	q_4	

	w_1	w_2	w_3	w_4	w_5
	w_9	w_8	w_7	w_6	
Sum	r_1	r_2	r_3	r_4	r_5
Difference	s_1	s_2	s_3	s_4	

	p_0	p_1	p_2		q_0	q_1	q_2
	p_5	p_4	p_3		q_4	q_3	
Sum	l_0	l_1	l_2	Sum	k_0	k_1	k_2
Difference	m_0	m_1	m_2				

	l_0		m_0	m_1		r_1	r_3
	l_1		m_2			r_5	
	l_2						
Sum	t_0	Sum	n_0	n_1	Sum	o_1	o_3

	s_1	s_2
	s_4	s_3
Sum	g_1	g_2
Difference	h_1	h_2

$20a_0 = t_0,$

$10a_1 = q_0 + q_1 \sin 72° + q_2 \sin 54° + q_3 \sin 36° + q_4 \sin 18°,$

$10a_2 = m_0 + m_1 \sin 54° + m_2 \sin 18°,$

$10a_3 = q_0 - q_3 \sin 72° - q_4 \sin 54° + q_1 \sin 36° - q_2 \sin 18°,$

$10a_4 = l_0 - l_2 \sin 54° + l_1 \sin 18°,$

$10a_5 = k_0 - k_2,$

$10a_6 = m_0 - m_2 \sin 54° - m_1 \sin 18°,$

$10a_7 = q_0 + q_3 \sin 72° - q_4 \sin 54° - q_1 \sin 36° - q_2 \sin 18°,$

$10a_8 = l_0 - l_1 \sin 54° + l_2 \sin 18°,$

$10a_9 = q_0 - q_1 \sin 72° + q_2 \sin 54° - q_3 \sin 36° + q_4 \sin 18°,$

$20a_{10} = n_0 - n_1,$

$10b_1 = r_5 + r_4 \sin 72° + r_3 \sin 54° + r_2 \sin 36° + r_1 \sin 18°,$

$10b_2 = g_2 \sin 72° + g_1 \sin 36°,$

$10b_3 = -r_5 + r_2 \sin 72° + r_1 \sin 54° - r_4 \sin 36° + r_3 \sin 18°,$

$10b_4 = h_1 \sin 72° + h_2 \sin 36°,$

$10b_5 = o_1 - o_3,$

$10b_6 = g_1 \sin 72° - g_2 \sin 36°,$

$10b_7 = -r_5 - r_2 \sin 72° + r_1 \sin 54° + r_4 \sin 36° + r_3 \sin 18°,$

$10b_8 = -h_2 \sin 72° + h_1 \sin 36°,$

$10b_9 = r_5 - r_4 \sin 72° + r_3 \sin 54° - r_2 \sin 36° + r_1 \sin 18°.$

24-ORDINATE SCHEME

	y_0	y_1	y_2	y_3	y_4	y_5	y_6	y_7	y_8	y_9	y_{10}	y_{11}	y_{12}
	y_{23}	y_{22}	y_{21}	y_{20}	y_{19}	y_{18}	y_{17}	y_{16}	y_{15}	y_{14}	y_{13}		
Sum	v_0	v_1	v_2	v_3	v_4	v_5	v_6	v_7	v_8	v_9	v_{10}	v_{11}	v_{12}
Difference		w_1	w_2	w_3	w_4	w_5	w_6	w_7	w_8	w_9	w_{10}	w_{11}	

v_0	v_1	v_2	v_3	v_4	v_5	v_6
v_{12}	v_{11}	v_{10}	v_9	v_8	v_7	

Sum	p_0	p_1	p_2	p_3	p_4	p_5	p_6
Difference	q_0	q_1	q_2	q_3	q_4	q_5	

w_1	w_2	w_3	w_4	w_5	w_6
w_{11}	w_{10}	w_9	w_8	w_7	

Sum	r_1	r_2	r_3	r_4	r_5	r_6
Difference	s_1	s_2	s_3	s_4	s_5	

p_0	p_1	p_2	p_3		s_1	s_2	s_3
p_6	p_5	p_4			s_5	s_4	

Sum	l_0	l_1	l_2	l_3	Sum	k_1	k_2	k_3
Difference	m_0	m_1	m_2		Difference	n_1	n_2	

l_0	l_1		m_0	m_1
l_3	l_2		m_2	

Sum	g_0	g_1	Sum	e_0	e_1
Difference	h_0	h_1	Difference	f_0	

$$24a_0 = g_0 + g_1,$$
$$12a_1 = q_0 + \tfrac{1}{2}q_4 + \tfrac{1}{2}\sqrt{2}\,q_3 + \tfrac{1}{2}\sqrt{3}\,q_2 + C_1 q_1 + C_2 q_5,$$
$$12a_2 = m_0 + \tfrac{1}{2}m_2 + \tfrac{1}{2}\sqrt{3}\,m_1,$$
$$12a_3 = q_0 - q_4 + \tfrac{1}{2}\sqrt{2}(q_1 - q_3 - q_5),$$
$$12a_4 = h_0 + \tfrac{1}{2}h_1,$$
$$12a_5 = q_0 + C_2 q_1 - \tfrac{1}{2}\sqrt{3}\,q_2 - \tfrac{1}{2}\sqrt{2}\,q_3 + \tfrac{1}{2}q_4 + C_1 q_5,$$
$$12a_6 = f_0,$$
$$12a_7 = q_0 - C_2 q_1 - \tfrac{1}{2}\sqrt{3}\,q_2 + \tfrac{1}{2}\sqrt{2}\,q_3 + \tfrac{1}{2}q_4 - C_1 q_5,$$
$$12a_8 = g_0 - \tfrac{1}{2}g_1,$$
$$12a_9 = q_0 - q_4 + \tfrac{1}{2}\sqrt{2}(-q_1 + q_3 + q_5),$$
$$12a_{10} = m_0 + \tfrac{1}{2}m_2 - \tfrac{1}{2}\sqrt{3}\,m_1,$$
$$12a_{11} = q_0 - C_1 q_1 + \tfrac{1}{2}\sqrt{3}\,q_2 - \tfrac{1}{2}\sqrt{2}\,q_3 + \tfrac{1}{2}q_4 - C_2 q_5,$$
$$24a_{12} = h_0 - h_1.$$

$$12b_1 = C_2r_1 + \tfrac{1}{2}r_2 + \tfrac{1}{2}\sqrt{2}r_3 + \tfrac{1}{2}\sqrt{3}r_4 + C_1r_5 + r_6,$$

$$12b_2 = \tfrac{1}{2}k_1 + \tfrac{1}{2}\sqrt{3}k_2 + k_3,$$

$$12b_3 = r_2 - r_6 + \tfrac{1}{2}\sqrt{2}(r_1 + r_3 - r_5),$$

$$12b_4 = \tfrac{1}{2}\sqrt{3}(n_1 + n_2),$$

$$12b_5 = C_1r_1 + \tfrac{1}{2}r_2 - \tfrac{1}{2}\sqrt{2}r_3 - \tfrac{1}{2}\sqrt{3}r_4 + C_2r_5 + r_6,$$

$$12b_6 = k_1 - k_3,$$

$$12b_7 = C_1r_1 - \tfrac{1}{2}r_2 - \tfrac{1}{2}\sqrt{2}r_3 + \tfrac{1}{2}\sqrt{3}r_4 + C_2r_5 - r_6,$$

$$12b_8 = \tfrac{1}{2}\sqrt{3}(n_1 - n_2),$$

$$12b_9 = r_6 - r_2 + \tfrac{1}{2}\sqrt{2}(r_1 + r_3 - r_5),$$

$$12b_{10} = s_3 + \tfrac{1}{2}(s_1 + s_5) - \tfrac{1}{2}\sqrt{3}(s_2 + s_4),$$

$$12b_{11} = C_2r_1 - \tfrac{1}{2}r_2 + \tfrac{1}{2}\sqrt{2}r_3 - \tfrac{1}{2}\sqrt{3}r_4 + C_1r_5 - r_6,$$

$$C_1 = \frac{\sqrt{3}+1}{2\sqrt{2}} = .96593,$$

$$C_2 = \frac{\sqrt{3}-1}{2\sqrt{2}} = .25882.$$

As an illustration let it be required to find a Fourier series of 24 terms to fit the data given in the table below.

$x°$	y	$x°$	y	$x°$	y	$x°$	y
00	149	90	159	180	178	270	179
15	137	105	178	195	170	285	185
30	128	120	189	210	177	300	182
45	126	135	191	225	183	315	176
60	128	150	189	240	181	330	166
75	135	165	187	255	179	345	160

149 137 128 126 128 135 159 178 189 191 189 187 178
　　160 166 176 182 185 179 179 181 183 177 170

v_0　149 297 294 302 310 320 338 357 370 374 366 357 178
w_1　　−23 −38 −50 −54 −50 −20 −1 8 8 12 17

	149	297	294	302	310	320	338
	178	357	366	374	370	357	
p_0	327	654	660	676	680	677	338
q_0	-29	-60	-72	-72	-60	-37	

	-23	-38	-50	-54	-50	-20
	17	12	8	8	-1	
r_1	-6	-26	-42	-46	-51	-20
s_1	-40	-50	-58	-62	-49	

	327	654	660	676		-40	-50	-58
	338	677	680			-49	-62	
l_0	665	1331	1340	676	k_1	-89	-112	-58
m_0	-11	-23	-20		n_1	9	12	

	665	1331		-11	-23
	676	1340		-20	
g_0	1341	2671	e_0	-31	-23
h_0	-11	-9	f_0	9	

The formula becomes

$$y = 167.167 - 19.983 \cos x - 3.410 \cos 2x + 5.470 \cos 3x$$
$$- 1.292 \cos 4x + .249 \cos 5x + .75 \cos 6x + .310 \cos 7x$$
$$+ .458 \cos 8x - .304 \cos 9x - .090 \cos 10x - .243 \cos 11x$$
$$- .083 \cos 12x - 12.779 \sin x - 16.624 \sin 2x - .323 \sin 3x$$
$$+ 1.516 \sin 4x + 1.461 \sin 5x - 2.583 \sin 6x + .321 \sin 7x$$
$$- .216 \sin 8x + .676 \sin 9x - .459 \sin 10x - .639 \sin 11x.$$

In what precedes the period was taken as 2π. This is not necessary; it may be any multiple of 2π. The process of finding a Fourier series of a limited number of terms which represent data whose period is not 2π will be best set forth by an example. In the table below the period is $\pi/3$ and the values of y are given at intervals of $\pi/18$. The 12-ordinate scheme can be used by first making the substitution

$$x = \tfrac{1}{3}\theta \text{ or } \theta = 3x.$$

$x°$	$θ°$	y	$x°$	$θ°$	y	$x°$	$θ°$	y
00	00	+27.2	40	120	+9.8	80	240	−11.5
10	30	+34.5	50	150	+8.5	90	270	−17.5
20	60	+21.5	60	180	+0.2	100	300	−17.2
30	90	+10.1	70	210	−7.1	110	330	+ 1.5

$$27.2 \quad 34.5 \quad 21.5 \quad 10.1 \quad 9.8 \quad 8.5 \quad 0.2$$
$$1.5 \quad -17.2 \quad -17.5 \quad -11.5 \quad -7.1$$

v_0 $27.2 \quad 36.0 \quad 4.3 \quad -7.4 \quad -1.7 \quad 1.4 \quad 0.2$

w_1 $33.0 \quad 38.7 \quad 27.6 \quad 21.3 \quad 15.6$

$$27.2 \quad 36.0 \quad 4.3 \quad -7.4$$
$$0.2 \quad 1.4 \quad -1.7$$

p_0 $27.4 \quad 37.4 \quad 2.6 \quad -7.4$

q_0 $27.0 \quad 34.6 \quad 6.0$

$$33.0 \quad 38.7 \quad 27.6 \qquad\qquad 27.4 \quad 37.4$$
$$15.6 \quad 21.3 \qquad\qquad\qquad 2.6 \quad -7.4$$

r_1 $48.6 \quad 60.0 \quad 27.6$ l_0 $30.0 \quad 30.0$

s_1 $17.4 \quad 17.4$

$$48.6 \quad 27.0$$
$$27.6 \quad 6.0$$

t_1 $21.0 \quad 21.0$

The formula is

$$y = 5 + 9.994 \cos θ + 8.7 \cos 2θ + 3.5 \cos 3θ + .006 \cos 5θ$$
$$+ 17.31 \sin θ + 5.023 \sin 2θ + 3.5 \sin 3θ - .01 \sin 5θ.$$

Replacing $θ$ by its value $3x$,

$$y = 5 + 9.994 \cos 3x + 8.7 \cos 6x + 3.5 \cos 9x + .006 \cos 15x$$
$$+ 17.31 \sin 3x + 5.023 \sin 6x + 3.5 \sin 9x - .01 \sin 15x.$$

CHAPTER VI

EMPIRICAL FORMULAS DEDUCED BY THE METHOD OF LEAST SQUARES

In the preceding chapters we computed approximately the values of constants in empirical formulas. The methods employed were almost wholly graphical, and although the results so obtained are satisfactory for most observational data, other methods must be employed when dealing with data of greater precision.

It is not the purpose of this chapter to develop the method of least squares, but only to show how to apply the method to observation equations so as to obtain the best values of the constants. For a discussion of the subject recourse must be had to one of the numerous books dealing with the method of least squares.*

It was found in Chapter I that the equation

$$y = a + bx + cx^2 \tag{1}$$

represents to a close approximation the relation between the values of x and y given by the data

x	y	x	y
0	3.1950	.5	3.2282
.1	3.2299	.6	3.1807
.2	3.2532	.7	3.1266
.3	3.2611	.8	3.0594
.4	3.2516	.9	2.9759

* Three well-known books are: Merriman, Method of Least Squares; Johnson, Theory of Errors and Method of Least Squares; Comstock, Method of Least Squares.

where x represents distance below the surface and y represents velocity in feet per second.

Substituting the above values of x and y in (1), the following ten linear observation equations are found:

$$a+\text{.0}b+\text{ .0}c=3.1950,$$
$$a+.1b+.01c=3.2299,$$
$$a+.2b+.04c=3.2532,$$
$$a+.3b+.09c=3.2611,$$
$$a+.4b+.16c=3.2516,$$
$$a+.5b+.25c=3.2282,$$
$$a+.6b+.36c=3.1807,$$
$$a+.7b+.49c=3.1266,$$
$$a+.8b+.64c=3.0594,$$
$$a+.9b+.81c=2.9759.$$

Here is presented the problem of the solution of a set of simultaneous equations in which the number of equations is greater than the number of unknown quantities. Any set of three equations selected from the ten will suffice for finding values of the unknown quantities. But the values so found will not satisfy any of the remaining seven equations. Since all of the equations are entitled to an equal amount of confidence it would manifestly be wrong to disregard or throw out any one of the equations. Any solution of the above set must include each one of the equations.

The problem is to combine the ten equations so as to obtain three equations which will yield the most probable values of the three unknown quantities a, b, and c. It is shown in works on the method of least squares that the first of such a set of equations is obtained by multiplying each one of the ten equations by the coefficient of a in that equation and adding the resulting equations. The second is obtained by multiplying each one of the ten equations by the coefficient of b in that equation and adding the equations so obtained. The third is obtained by multiplying each of the ten equations by the coefficient of

c in that equation and adding the equation so obtained. **The** process of computing the coefficients in the three equations is shown in the table. The coefficients of a, b, and c are represented by A, B, and C respectively, and the right-hand members are designated by N. The number S, which stands for the numerical sum of A, B, C and N, is introduced as a check on the work. It must be remembered that this method of finding the values of the constants holds only for linear equations.

The sum of the numbers in the column headed $AA = \Sigma AA$ $= 10$. The sum of the numbers in the column headed $AB = \Sigma AB = 4.5$. The sum of the numbers in the column headed $AC = \Sigma AC = 2.85$. Also the sum of the numbers in the column headed $AN = \Sigma AN = 31.7616$. These sums give the coefficients in the first equation.* The second and third equations are obtained in the same way.

The three equations from which we obtain the most probable values of the constants are:

$$10\ a\ +\ 4.5b\ +2.85c\ =31.7616;$$
$$4.5a\ +2.85b\ +2.025c\ =14.08957;$$
$$2.85a\ +2.025b+1.5333c=\ 8.828813.$$

These are called normal equations. From them are obtained

$$a=+3.19513;$$
$$b=+\ .44254;$$
$$c=-\ .76531.$$

The check for the first equation is

$$\Sigma AA+\Sigma AB+\Sigma AC+\Sigma AN=\Sigma AS=49.1116;$$

for the second equation

$$\Sigma AB+\Sigma BB+\Sigma BC+\Sigma BN=\Sigma BS=23.46457;$$

for the third equation

$$\Sigma AC+\Sigma BC+\Sigma CC+\Sigma CN=\Sigma CS=15.237113.$$

* Cf. Wright and Hayford, Adjustment of Observations.

AA	AB	AC	AN	AS
1	0	0	3.1950	4.1950
1	.1	.01	3.2299	4.3399
1	.2	.04	3.2532	4.4932
1	.3	.09	3.2611	4.6511
1	.4	.16	3.2516	4.8116
1	.5	.25	3.2282	4.9782
1	.6	.36	3.1807	5.1407
1	.7	.49	3.1266	5.3166
1	.8	.64	3.0594	5.4994
1	.9	.81	2.9759	5.6859
10	4.5	2.85	31.7616	49.1116

AB	BB	BC	BN	BS
	0	0	0	0
	.01	.001	.32299	.43399
	.04	.008	.65064	.89864
	.09	.027	.97833	1.39533
	.16	.064	1.30064	1.92464
	.25	.125	1.61410	2.48910
	.36	.216	1.90842	3.08442
	.49	.343	2.18862	3.72162
	.64	.512	2.44752	4.39952
	.81	.729	2.67831	5.11731
4.5	2.85	2.025	14.08957	23.46457

AC	BC	CC	CN	CS
		0	0	0
		.0001	.032299	.043399
		.0016	.130128	.179728
		.0081	.293499	.418599
		.0256	.520256	.769856
		.0625	.807050	1.244550
		.1296	1.145052	1.850652
		.2401	1.532034	2.605134
		.4096	1.958016	3.519616
		.6561	2.410479	4.605579
2.85	2.025	1.5333	8.828813	15.237113

The formula is

$$y = 3.19513 + .44254x - .76531x^2.$$

For the purpose of comparison the observed values and the computed values are written in the table. v (called residual) stands for the observed value minus the value computed from the formula.

x	Observed y	Computed y	v	v^2
0	3.1950	3.1951	$-.0001$	.00000001
.1	3.2299	3.2317	$-.0018$	.00000324
.2	3.2532	3.2530	$+.0002$	.00000004
.3	3.2611	3.2590	$+.0021$	.00000441
.4	3.2516	3.2497	$+.0019$	.00000361
.5	3.2282	3.2251	$+.0031$	.00000961
.6	3.1807	3.1851	$-.0044$	.00001936
.7	3.1266	3.1299	$-.0033$	.00001089
.8	3.0594	3.0594	.0000	.00000000
.9	2.9759	2.9735	$+.0024$	.00000576
			$+.0001$	.00005493

This method derives its name from the fact that the sum of the squares of the residuals is a minimum. A discussion of this will be found in the books referred to above.

In case the formula selected to express the relation between the variables is not linear the method of least squares cannot be applied directly. In order to apply the method the formula must be expanded by means of Taylor's Theorem. Even when the formula is linear in the constants it may be advantageous to make use of Taylor's Theorem. In order to make this transformation clear we will apply it to the formula just considered.

Suppose that there have been found approximate values of a, b, and c, a_0, b_0 and c_0, say, then it is evident that corrections must be added in order to obtain the most probable values of the constants. Let the corrections be represented by Δa, Δb, and Δc. And let

$$a = a_0 + \Delta a,$$
$$b = b_0 + \Delta b,$$
$$c = c_0 + \Delta c.$$

The formula was
$$y = a + bx + cx^2.$$

This may be written

$$y = f(a, b, c) = f(a_0 + \Delta a, \ b_0 + \Delta b, \ c_0 + \Delta c).$$

Expanding the right-hand member

$$f(a_0 + \Delta a, \ b_0 + \Delta b, \ c_0 + \Delta c) = f(a_0, b_0, c_0) + \frac{\partial f}{\partial a_0}\Delta a + \frac{\partial f}{\partial b_0}\Delta b + \frac{\partial f}{\partial c_0}\Delta c$$

$$+ \frac{1}{\lfloor 2} \left[\frac{\partial^2 f}{\partial a_0{}^2}(\Delta a)^2 + \frac{\partial^2 f}{\partial b_0{}^2}(\Delta b)^2 + \frac{\partial^2 f}{\partial c_0{}^2}(\Delta c)^2 + \frac{\partial^2 f}{\partial a_0 \partial b_0}(\Delta a \Delta b) \right.$$

$$\left. + \frac{\partial^2 f}{\partial a_0 \partial c_0}(\Delta a \Delta c) + \frac{\partial^2 f}{\partial b_0 \partial c_0}(\Delta b \Delta c) \right] + \cdots$$

where $\dfrac{\partial f}{\partial a_0}$ stands for the value of the partial derivative of $f(a, b, c)$ with respect to a and a_0 substituted for a, $\dfrac{\partial^2 f}{\partial a_0{}^2}$ stands for the value of the second partial derivative of $f(a, b, c)$ with respect to a and a_0 substituted for a, etc. If a_0, b_0, and c_0 have been found to a sufficiently close approximation the second and higher powers of the corrections may be neglected.

$$\frac{\partial f}{\partial a_0} = 1;$$

$$\frac{\partial f}{\partial b_0} = x;$$

$$\frac{\partial f}{\partial c_0} = x^2;$$

The formula becomes

$$y - f(a_0, b_0, c_0) = \frac{\partial f}{\partial a_0}\Delta a + \frac{\partial f}{\partial b_0}\Delta b + \frac{\partial f}{\partial c_0}\Delta c,$$

or

$$y - (a_0 + b_0 x + c_0 x^2) = \Delta a + x\Delta b + x^2 \Delta c.$$

Selecting for the values of a_0, b_0, and c_0 those found in Chapter I, the new set of observation equations are

$$\Delta a + o\Delta b + o\Delta c = .0002,$$

$$\Delta a + .1\Delta b + .01\Delta c = -.0013,$$

$$\Delta a + .2\Delta b + .04\Delta c = .0008,$$

$$\Delta a + .3\Delta b + .09\Delta c = .0027,$$

$$\Delta a + .4\Delta b + .16\Delta c = .0024,$$

$$\Delta a + .5\Delta b + .25\Delta c = .0034,$$

$$\Delta a + .6\Delta b + .36\Delta c = -.0045,$$

$$\Delta a + .7\Delta b + .49\Delta c = -.0038,$$

$$\Delta a + .8\Delta b + .64\Delta c = -.0010,$$

$$\Delta a + .9\Delta b + .81\Delta c = .0007.$$

From these are obtained the three normal equations

$$10\Delta a + 4.5 \ \Delta b + 2.85 \ \Delta c = -.0004,$$

$$4.5\Delta a + 2.85 \ \Delta b + 2.025 \ \Delta c = -.00203,$$

$$2.85\Delta a + 2.025\Delta b + 1.5333\Delta c = -.002059.$$

Solving

$$\Delta a = +.00033,$$

$$\Delta b = +.00254,$$

$$\Delta c = -.00531,$$

which added to the values of a_0, b_0, and c_0, give

$$a = 3.19513,$$

$$b = .44254,$$

$$c = -.76531.$$

the same as just found.

The above process may be applied to linear equations containing more than three constants. But as the method of procedure is quite evident from the above the general statement of the process will be made with reference to equations containing only three constants.

Let the observation equations be represented by

$$a_1x + b_1y + c_1z = n_1 \quad p_1,$$

$$a_2x + b_2y + c_2z = n_2 \quad p_2,$$

$$a_3x + b_3y + c_3z = n_3 \quad p_3,$$

$$\cdot \quad \cdot \quad \cdot \quad \cdot \quad \cdot \quad \cdot \quad \cdot$$

$$\cdot \quad \cdot \quad \cdot \quad \cdot \quad \cdot \quad \cdot \quad \cdot$$

$$a_mx + b_my + c_mz = n_m \quad p_m.$$

The normal equations will then be

$$\Sigma pa^2 \cdot x + \Sigma pab \cdot y + \Sigma pac \cdot z = \Sigma pan,$$

$$\Sigma pab \cdot x + \Sigma pb^2 \cdot y + \Sigma pbc \cdot z = \Sigma pbn,$$

$$\Sigma pac \cdot x + \Sigma pbc \cdot y + \Sigma pc^2 \cdot z = \Sigma pcn,$$

where a, b, c, and n are observed quantities, and x, y, and z are to be determined, p_1, p_2, p_3 . . . p_m are the weights assigned to the observation equations. In the problem treated at the beginning of the chapter the weight of each equation was taken as unity.

It was stated on a preceding page that when a formula to be fitted to a set of observations is not linear in the constants it must be expanded by Taylor's Theorem.

Take as an illustration a problem considered in Chapter IV. The formula considered was

$$y = f(A, B, m, n) = Ax^m + Bx^n,$$

$$\frac{\partial f}{\partial A_0} = x^{m_0},$$

$$\frac{\partial f}{\partial B_0} = x^{n_0},$$

$$\frac{\partial f}{\partial m_0} = A_0 x^{m_0} \log x,$$

$$\frac{\partial f}{\partial n_0} = B_0 x^{n_0} \log x;$$

$$y = f(A, B, m, n) \quad = f(A_0, B_0, m_0, n_0) + \frac{\partial f}{\partial A_0}\Delta A + \frac{\partial f}{\partial B_0}\Delta B$$

$$+ \frac{\partial f}{\partial m_0}\Delta m + \frac{\partial f}{\partial n_0}\Delta n;$$

$$y - f(A_0, B_0, m_0, n_0) = \frac{\partial f}{\partial A_0}\Delta A + \frac{\partial f}{\partial B_0}\Delta B + \frac{\partial f}{\partial m_0}\Delta m + \frac{\partial f}{\partial n_0}\Delta n.$$

The observation equations will be of the form

$$\frac{\partial f}{\partial A_0}\Delta A + \frac{\partial f}{\partial B_0}\Delta B + \frac{\partial f}{\partial m_0}\Delta m + \frac{\partial f}{\partial n_0}\Delta n = y - yo.$$

Assume the approximate values found in Chapter IV.

$$A = 1.522,$$
$$B = -.685,$$
$$m = .55,$$
$$n = 1.4.$$

x	.05	.10	.15	.20	.25	.30
$x^{.55}$	.19	.28	.35	.41	.47	.52
$x^{.14}$	.02	.04	.07	.10	.14	.19
A_0	1.522					
B_0	− .685					
$\log x$	−2.996	−2.303	−1.897	−1.609	−1.386	−1.204
$A_0 x^{m_0} \log x$	− .88	− .99	−1.02	−1.01	− .98	− .94
$B_0 x^{n_0} \log x$	.03	.06	.09	.12	.14	.15

x	.35	.40	.45	.50	.55
$x^{.55}$	.56	.60	.64	.68	.72
$x^{.14}$	.23	.28	.33	.38	.43
$\log x$	−1.050	−0.916	−0.799	−0.693	−0.598
$A_0 x^{m_0} \log x$	− .90	− .84	− .78	− .72	− .66
$B_0 x^{n_0} \log x$	.16	.17	.18	.18	.18

The new observation equations become

$$.19\Delta A + .02\Delta B - .88\Delta m + .03\Delta n = .0004,$$
$$.28\Delta A + .04\Delta B - .99\Delta m + .06\Delta n = .0002,$$
$$.35\Delta A + .07\Delta B - 1.02\Delta m + .09\Delta n = -.0001,$$

$$.41\Delta A + .10\Delta B - 1.01\Delta m + .12\Delta n = \quad .0000,$$
$$.47\Delta A + .14\Delta B - \quad .98\Delta m + .14\Delta n = \quad .0013,$$
$$.52\Delta A + .19\Delta B - \quad .94\Delta m + .15\Delta n = -.0001,$$
$$.56\Delta A + .23\Delta B - \quad .90\Delta m + .16\Delta n = -.0019,$$
$$.60\Delta A + .28\Delta B - \quad .84\Delta m + .17\Delta n = -.0016,$$
$$.64\Delta A + .33\Delta B - \quad .78\Delta m + .18\Delta n = -.0001,$$
$$.68\Delta A + .38\Delta B - \quad .72\Delta m + .18\Delta n = -.0001.$$
$$.72\Delta A + .43\Delta B - \quad .66\Delta m + .18\Delta n = \quad .0011.$$

From these the four normal equations are obtained

$$2.960\Delta A + 1.321\Delta B - 4.637\Delta m + .806\Delta n = -.00071,$$
$$1.321\Delta A + \quad .642\Delta B - 1.802\Delta m + .359\Delta n = -.00031,$$
$$-4.637\Delta A - 1.802\Delta B + 8.737\Delta m - 1.253\Delta n = +.00085,$$
$$.806\Delta A + \quad .359\Delta B - 1.253\Delta m + .221\Delta n = -.00023.$$

From which

$$\Delta A = -.0068,$$
$$\Delta B = +.0112,$$
$$\Delta m = -.0022,$$
$$\Delta n = -.0070.$$

These corrections being applied the final formula becomes

$$y = 1.5152x^{.5478} - .6738x^{1.393}.$$

CHAPTER VII

INTERPOLATION.—DIFFERENTIATION OF TABULATED FUNCTIONS

INTERPOLATION

In Chapter II we found that the formula

XI. $$y = \frac{x}{.025 + .2525x + 2.5x^2}$$

represents to a fair degree of approximation the values of y given by the data. Any other value of y, within the range of values given, can be obtained in the same way. This rests on the assumption that the formula derived expresses the law connecting x and y. For example, the value of y corresponding to $x = 1.05$ will be

$$y = \frac{1.05}{.025 + .2525(1.05) + 2.5(1.05)^2} = 0.345.$$

When a formula is used for the purpose of obtaining values of y, within the range of the data given it is called an interpolation formula. Interpolation denotes the process of calculating under some assumed law, any term of a series from values of any other terms supposed given.* It is evident that empirical formulas cannot safely be used for obtaining values outside of the range of the data from which they were derived.

* For a more extended discussion of the subject the reader is referred to Text-book of the Institute of Actuaries, part II (1st ed. 1887, 2nd ed. 1902), p. 434; Encyklopädie der Mathematischen Wissenchaften, Vol. I, pp. 799–820; Encyclopedia Britannica; T. N. Thiele, Interpolationsrechnung.

As to relative accuracy of different formulas, see Proceedings London Mathematical Society (2) Vol. IV., p. 320.

There are two convenient formulas for interpolation which will be developed.*

The first one of these requires the expression for y_{x+n} in terms of y_x and its successive differences. y_x represents the value of a function of x for any chosen value of x, and y_{x+n} represents the value of that function when $x+n$ has been substituted for x.

$$y_{x+1} = y_x + \Delta y_x;$$

$$y_{x+2} = y_x + \Delta y_x + \Delta(y_x + \Delta y_x)$$
$$= y_x + 2\Delta y_x + \Delta^2 y_x;$$

$$y_{x+3} = y_x + 2\Delta y_x + \Delta^2 y_x + \Delta(y_x + 2\Delta y_x + \Delta^2 y_x)$$
$$= y_x + 3\Delta y_x + 3\Delta^2 y_x + \Delta^3 y_x;$$

$$y_{x+4} = y_x + 3\Delta y_x + 3\Delta^2 y_x + \Delta^3 y_x + \Delta(y_x + 3\Delta y_x + 3\Delta^2 y_x + \Delta^3 y_x)$$
$$= y_x + 4\Delta y_x + 6\Delta^2 y_x + 4\Delta^3 y_x + \Delta^4 y_x.$$

These results suggest, by their resemblance to the binomial expression, the general formula

$$y_{x+n} = y_x + n\Delta y_x + \frac{n(n-1)}{\lfloor 2} \Delta^2 y_x + \frac{n(n-1)(n-2)}{\lfloor 3} \Delta^3 y_x + \text{etc.}$$

If we suppose this theorem true for a particular value of n, then for the next greater value we have

$$y_{x+n+1} = y_x + n\Delta y_x + \frac{n(n-1)}{\lfloor 2} \Delta^2 y_x + \frac{n(n-1)(n-2)}{\lfloor 3} \Delta^3 y_x + \text{etc.},$$

$$+ \Delta y_x + n\Delta^2 y_x + \frac{n(n-1)}{\lfloor 2} \Delta^3 y_x + \text{etc.},$$

$$= y_x + (n+1)\Delta y_x + \frac{(n+1)n}{\lfloor 2} \Delta^2 y_x + \frac{(n+1)n(n-1)}{\lfloor 3} \Delta^3 y_x + \text{etc.}$$

The form of the last result shows that the theorem remains true for the next greater value of n, and therefore for the next

* See Chapter III, Boole's Finite Differences.

greater value. But it is ·true when $n=4$, therefore it is true when $n=5$. Since it is true for $n=5$ it is true when $n=6$, étc.

If now o is substituted for x and x for n, it follows that

$$y_x = y_0 + x\Delta y_0 + \frac{x(x-1)}{\underline{|2}}\Delta^2 y_0 + \frac{x(x-1)(x-2)}{\underline{|3}}\Delta^3 y_0 + \text{etc.}$$

If $\Delta^n y. = 0$, the right-hand member of the above equation is a rational integral function of x of degree $n-1$. The formula becomes

$$y_x = y_0 + x\Delta y_0 + \frac{x(x-1)}{\underline{|2}}\Delta^2 y_0 + \frac{x(x-1)(x-2)}{\underline{|3}}\Delta^3 y_0 + \ldots$$

$$+ \frac{x(x-1)(x-2) \ldots (x-n+2)}{\underline{|n-1}}\Delta^{n-1} y_0. \ldots \ldots \quad (1)$$

Formula (1) will now be applied to problems. *It must not be forgotten that in applying this formula x is taken to represent the distance of the term required from the first term in the series, the common distance of the terms given being taken as unity.*

1. Required to find the value of y corresponding to $x=.425$ having given the values under XIX. In the interpolation formula $x=.5$.

y_0	y_1	y_2	y_3
·730	·757	·780	·800
Δy_0..... .027	.023	.020	
$\Delta^2 y_0$..... $-.004$	$-.003$		
$\Delta^3 y_0$..... .001			

$$y = y_0 + \tfrac{1}{2}\Delta y_0 - \tfrac{1}{8}\Delta^2 y_0 + \tfrac{1}{16}\Delta^3 y_0$$

$$= .730 + .0135 + .0005 + .0001$$

$$= .744.$$

This is the same as given by XIX.

2. Find the value of y corresponding to $x=2.3$. x in the formula will have the value $\tfrac{3}{5}$ if we take $y_0 = -.1826$ when $x=2$.

y_0	y_1	y_2	y_3	y_4	y_5
$-.1826$	$-.4463$	$-.7039$	$-.9582$	-1.2119	-1.4677

Δy_0	$-.2637$	$-.2576$	$-.2543$	$-.2537$	$-.2558$
$\Delta^2 y_0$	$.0061$	$.0033$	$.0006$	$-.0021$	
$\Delta^3 y_0$	$-.0028$	$-.0027$	$-.0027$		
$\Delta^4 y_0$	$.0001$	$.0000$			
$\Delta^5 y_0$	$-.0001$				

$$y_x = y_0 + x\Delta y_0 + \frac{x(x-1)}{\underline{2}}\Delta^2 y_0 + \frac{x(x-1)(x-2)}{\underline{3}}\Delta^3 y_0$$

$$+ \frac{x(x-1)(x-2)(x-3)}{\underline{4}}\Delta^4 y_0 + \text{etc.}$$

$$= -.1826 + \tfrac{3}{5}(-.2637) + \frac{\tfrac{3}{5}(-\tfrac{2}{5})}{2}(.0061) + \frac{\tfrac{3}{5}(-\tfrac{2}{5})(-\tfrac{7}{5})}{6}(-.0028)$$

$$+ \frac{\tfrac{3}{5}(-\tfrac{2}{5})(-\tfrac{7}{5})(-\tfrac{12}{5})}{24}(.0001)$$

$$= -.3417.$$

3. The following example is taken from Boole's Finite Differences. Given $\log 3.14 = .4969296$, $\log 3.15 = .4983106$, $\log 3.16 = .4996871$, $\log 3.17 = .5010593$; required an approximate value of $\log 3.14159$.

	y_0	y_1	y_2	y_3
	$.4969296$	$.4983106$	$.4996871$	$.5010593$
Δy_0.........	$.0013810$	$.0013765$	$.0013722$	
$\Delta^2 y_0$........	$-.0000045$	$-.0000043$		
$\Delta^3 y_0$........	$.0000002$			

Here the value of x in the formula is equal to 0.159.

$$y_x = .4969296 + (.159)(.0013810) + \frac{(.159)(.159-1)}{2}(-.0000045)$$

$$+ \frac{.159(.159-1)(.159-2)}{6}(.0000002)$$

$$= .4971495.$$

This is correct to the last decimal place. If only two terms had been used in the right-hand member of the formula, which is equivalent to the rule of proportional parts, there would have been an error of 3 in the last decimal place. The rapid decrease in the value of the differences enables us to judge quite well of the accuracy of the results. The above formula can be applied only when the values of x form an arithmetical series.

In case the series of values given are not equidistant, that is, the values of the independent variable do not form an arithmetical series, it becomes necessary to apply another formula.

Let y_a, y_b, y_c, y_d, . . . y_k be the given values corresponding to a, b, c, d, . . . k respectively as values of x. It is required to find an approximate expression for y_x, an unknown term corresponding to a value of x between $x = a$ and $x = k$.

Since there are n conditions to be satisfied the expression which is to represent all of the values must contain n constants. Assume as the general expression

$$y_x = A + Bx + Cx^2 + Dx^3 + \ldots + Nx^{n-1}.$$

Geometrically this is equivalent to drawing through the n points represented by the n sets of corresponding values a parabola of degree $n - 1$.

Substituting the sets of values given by the data in the equation above n equations are obtained from which to determine the values of A, B, C, etc.,

$$y_a = A + Ba + Ca^2 + Da^3 + \ldots Na^{n-1};$$
$$y_b = A + Bb + Cb^2 + Db^3 + \ldots Nb^{n-1};$$
$$\cdot \quad \cdot \quad \cdot \quad \cdot \quad \cdot \quad \cdot \quad \cdot$$
$$\cdot \quad \cdot \quad \cdot \quad \cdot \quad \cdot \quad \cdot \quad \cdot$$
$$y_k = A + Bk + Ck^2 + Dk^3 + \ldots Nk^{n-1}.$$

But the solution of these equations would require a great deal of work which can be avoided by using another but equivalent form of equation.

$$\text{Let } y_x = A(x-b)(x-c)(x-d) \ldots (x-k)$$
$$+B(x-a)(x-c)(x-d) \ldots (x-k)$$
$$+C(x-a)(x-b)(x-d) \ldots (x-k)$$
$$+D(x-a)(x-b)(x-c) \ldots (x-k)$$
$$+ \text{ etc. to } n \text{ terms.}$$

Each one of the n terms on the right-hand side of the equation lacks one of the factors $x-a,\ x-b,\ x-c,\ x-d,\ \ldots x-k,$ and each is affected with an arbitrary constant. The expression on the right-hand side of the equation is a rational integral function of x.

Letting $x = a$ gives

$$y_a = A(a-b)(a-c)(a-d) \ldots a-k,$$

and

$$A = \frac{y_a}{(a-b)(a-c)(a-d) \ldots a-k}.$$

Letting $x = b$ gives

$$B = \frac{y_b}{(b-a)(b-c)(b-d) \ldots (b-k)}.$$

Proceeding in the same way we obtain values for all of the constants and, finally,

$$y_x = y_a\frac{(x-b)(x-c)(x-d) \ldots (x-k)}{(a-b)(a-c)(a-d) \ldots (a-k)}$$
$$+y_b\frac{(x-a)(x-c)(x-d) \ldots (x-k)}{(b-a)(b-c)(b-d) \ldots (b-k)}$$
$$+y_c\frac{(x-a)(x-b)(x-d) \ldots (x-k)}{(c-a)(c-b)(c-d) \ldots (c-k)}$$
$$+y_d\frac{(x-a)(x-b)(x-c) \ldots (x-k)}{(d-a)(d-b)(d-c) \ldots (d-k)}$$
$$\cdot \qquad \cdot \qquad \cdot \qquad \cdot \qquad \cdot$$
$$\cdot \qquad \cdot \qquad \cdot \qquad \cdot \qquad \cdot$$
$$+y_k\frac{(x-a)(x-b)(x-c) \ldots}{(k-a)(k-b)(k-c) \ldots} \ldots \qquad \ldots \ldots \quad (2)$$

This is called Lagrange's theorem for interpolation.

1. Apply formula (2) to the data given under formula XIX for finding the value of y corresponding to $x = 0.425$. Select two values on either side of the value required,

$$a = .35, \quad y_a = .695,$$
$$b = .40, \quad y_b = .730,$$
$$c = .45, \quad y_c = .757,$$
$$d = .50, \quad y_d = .780.$$

x in the formula must be taken as 0.5.

$$y = (.695)\frac{\frac{1}{2}(-\frac{1}{2})(-\frac{3}{2})}{(-1)(-2)(-3)} + (.730)\frac{\frac{3}{2}(-\frac{1}{2})(-\frac{3}{2})}{(1)(-1)(-2)}$$
$$+ (.757)\frac{(\frac{3}{2})(\frac{1}{2})(-\frac{3}{2})}{(2)(1)(-1)} \quad + (.780)\frac{(\frac{3}{2})(\frac{1}{2})(-\frac{1}{2})}{(3)(2)(1)}$$
$$= .744.$$

2. Required an approximate value of $\log 212$ from the following data:

$$\log 210 = 2.3222193,$$
$$\log 211 = 2.3242825,$$
$$\log 213 = 2.3283796,$$
$$\log 214 = 2.3304138.$$

$$\log 212 = (2.3222193)\frac{(1)(-1)(-2)}{(-1)(-3)(-4)} + (2.3242825)\frac{(2)(-1)(-2)}{(1)(-2)(-3)}$$
$$+ (2.3283796)\frac{(2)(1)(-2)}{(3)(2)(-1)} \quad + (2.3304138)\frac{(2)(1)(-1)}{(4)(3)(1)}$$
$$= 2.326359.$$

This is correct to the last figure.

In case the values given are periodic it is better to use a formula involving circular functions. In Chapter V the approximate values of the constants in formula XX were derived. This formula could be used as an interpolation formula. But on account of the work involved in determining the constants it is much more convenient to use an equivalent one which does not necessitate the determination of constants.* The equivalent formula given by Gauss is

$$y_x = y_a \frac{\sin \frac{1}{2}(x-b) \sin \frac{1}{2}(x-c) \ldots \sin \frac{1}{2}(x-k)}{\sin \frac{1}{2}(a-b) \sin \frac{1}{2}(a-c) \ldots \sin \frac{1}{2}(a-k)}$$

$$+ y_b \frac{\sin \frac{1}{2}(x-a) \sin \frac{1}{2}(x-c) \ldots \sin \frac{1}{2}(x-k)}{\sin \frac{1}{2}(b-a) \sin \frac{1}{2}(b-c) \ldots \sin \frac{1}{2}(b-k)}$$

$$+ y_c \frac{\sin \frac{1}{2}(x-a) \sin \frac{1}{2}(x-b) \ldots \sin \frac{1}{2}(x-k)}{\sin \frac{1}{2}(c-a) \sin \frac{1}{2}(c-b) \ldots \sin \frac{1}{2}(c-k)}$$

$$+ \text{etc.} \quad \ldots \ldots \ldots \ldots \ldots \ldots \quad (3)$$

It is evident that the value of y_a is obtained from this formula by putting $x = a$. The value of y_b is obtained by putting $x = b$, and y_c by putting $x = c$.

The proof that (3) is equivalent to XX need not be given here.

Let it be required to find an approximate value of y corresponding to $x = 42°$ from the values given.

x	y
$30°$	10.1
$40°$	9.8
$50°$	8.5

From (3)

$$y = (10.1) \frac{\sin 1° \sin (-4°)}{\sin (-5°) \sin(-10°)} + (9.8) \frac{\sin 6° \sin (-4°)}{\sin 5° \sin (-5°)}$$

$$+ (8.5) \frac{\sin 6° \sin 1°}{\sin 10° \sin 5°}$$

$$= -(10.1) \frac{(.0175)(.0698)}{(.0872)(.1736)} + (9.8) \frac{(.1045)(.0698)}{(.0872)^2}$$

$$+ (8.5) \frac{(.1045)(.0175)}{(.1736)(.0872)}$$

$$= 9.618.$$

* Trigometrische Interpolation, Encyklopädie der Mathematischen Wissenchaften, Vol. II, pt. I, pp. 642–693.

A better result would have been obtained by using four sets of values.

DIFFERENTIATION OF TABULATED FUNCTIONS

It is frequently desirable to obtain the first and second derivatives of a tabulated function to a closer approximation than graphical methods will yield. For that purpose we will derive differentiation formulas from (1) and (2). From

$$y_x = y_0 + x\Delta y_0 + \frac{x(x-1)}{\lfloor 2}\Delta^2 y_0 + \frac{x(x-1)(x-2)}{\lfloor 3}\Delta^3 y_0$$

$$+ \frac{x(x-1)(x-2)(x-3)}{\lfloor 4}\Delta^4 y_0 + \ldots$$

$$+ \frac{x(x-1)(x-2) \ldots (x-n+2)}{\lfloor n-1}\Delta^{n-1} y_0. \quad \ldots \quad (1)$$

By differentiating it follows that

$$y'_x = \Delta y_0 + \frac{2x-1}{2}\Delta^2 y_0 + \frac{3x^2-6x+2}{\lfloor 3}\Delta^3 y_0$$

$$+ \frac{4x^3-12x^2+22x-6}{\lfloor 4}\Delta^4 y_0 + \ldots \quad \ldots \quad \ldots \quad (4)$$

Differentiating again

$$y_x'' = \Delta^2 y_0 + (x-1)\Delta^3 y_0 + (\tfrac{1}{2}x^2-x+\tfrac{11}{12})\Delta^4 y_0 + \ldots \quad \ldots \quad (5)$$

As an illustration let it be required to find the first and second derivatives of the function given in the table below and determine whether the series of observations is periodic.*

The consecutive daily observations of a function being 0.099833, 0.208460, 0.314566, 0.416871, 0.514136, 0.605186, 0.688921, 0.764329, show that the function is periodic and determine its period.

* Interpolation and Numerical Integration, by David Gibb.

From the given observations the following table may be written:

x	$y=f(x)$	Δ	Δ^2	Δ^3	Δ^4
1	0.099833				
		0.108627			
2	0.208460		$-.002521$		
		0.106106		$-.001280$	
3	0.314566		$-.003801$		.000041
		0.102305		$(+)-.001239$	
4	0.416871		$-.005040$		.000064
		$(-)0.097265$		$(+)-.001175$	
5	0.514136		$-.006215$		.000075
		$(-)0.091050$		$(+)-.001100$	
6	0.605186		$-.007315$		.000088
		$(-)0.083735$		$(+)-.001012$	
7	0.688921		$-.008327$		
		$(-)0.075408$			
8	0.764329				

From (4)

$y'_1 =$ .108627 $-.000427$ $y'_2 =$ .106106 $-.000413$
         .001260 $-.000010$ .001900 $-.000016$

         .109887 $-.000437$ .108006 $-.000429$
     $-.000437$ $-.000429$

         .109450   .107577

$y'_3 =$ .102305 $-.000392$ $y'_4 =$ .097265 $-.000367$
         .002520 $-.000019$ .003108 $-.000022$

         .104825 $-.000411$ .100373 $-.000389$
     $-.000411$ $-.000389$

         .104414   .099984

For the remaining first derivatives the order must be reversed and the resulting sign changed.

$y'_5 = -.097265$ .002520 $y'_6 = -.091050$ .003108
        $-.000010$ .000413 $-.000016$ .000392

        $-.097275$ .002933 $-.091066$ .003500
           .002933   .003500

           .094342   .087566

$y'_7 = -.083735$ $.003658$ $y'_8 = -.075408$ $.004164$

$-.000019$ $.000367$ $-.000022$ $.000337$

$-.083754$ $.004025$ $-.075430$ $.004501$

$.004025$ $.004501$

$.079729$ $.070929$

From (5)

$y''_1 = -.002521$ $.001280$ $y''_2 = -.003801$ $.001239$

$.001318$ $.000038$ $.001298$ $.000059$

$-.001203$ $.001318$ $-.002503$ $.001298$

$y''_3 = -.005040$ $.001175$ $y''_4 = -.006215$ $.001100$

$.001244$ $.000069$ $.001181$ $.000081$

$-.003796$ $.001244$ $-.005034$ $.001181$

$y''_5 = -.005040$ $y''_6 = -.006215$

$-.001239$ $-.001175$

$-.006279$ $-.007390$

$.000038$ $.000059$

$-.006241$ $-.007331$

$y''_7 = -.007315$ $y''_8 = -.008327$

$-.001100$ $-.001012$

$-.008415$ $-.009339$

$.000069$ $.000081$

$-.008346$ $-.009258$

x	y	y'	y''	$\dfrac{y''}{y}$
1	.099833	.109450	$-.001203$	$-.0121$
2	.208460	.107577	$-.002503$	$-.0120$
3	.314566	.104414	$-.003796$	$-.0121$
4	.416871	.099984	$-.005034$	$-.0121$

x	y	y'	y''	$\dfrac{y''}{y}$
5	.514136	.094342	$-.006241$	$-.0121$
6	.605186	.087566	$-.007331$	$-.0121$
7	.688921	.079729	$-.008346$	$-.0121$
8	.764329	.070929	$-.009258$	$-.0121$

Since $\dfrac{y''}{y}$ is very nearly constant and equal to $-.0121$, the corresponding differential equation is

$$y''+.0121y=0,$$

whose solution is

$$y=A \cos 0.11x+B \sin 0.11x.$$

This shows that y is a period function of x, and its period is $\dfrac{2\pi}{0.11}$, or 57.12 days.

Convenient formulas for the first and second derivatives may also be obtained by differentiating Lagrange's formula for interpolation. Using five points the formula is

$$y_x=y_a\frac{(x-b)(x-c)(x-d)(x-e)}{(a-b)(a-c)(a-d)(a-e)}+y_b\frac{(x-a)(x-c)(x-d)(x-e)}{(b-a)(b-c)(b-d)(b-e)}$$

$$+y_c\frac{(x-a)(x-b)(x-d)(x-e)}{(c-a)(c-b)(c-d)(c-e)}+y_d\frac{(x-a)(x-b)(x-c)(x-e)}{(d-a)(d-b)(d-c)(d-e)}$$

$$+y_e\frac{(x-a)(x-b)(x-c)(x-d)}{(e-a)(e-b)(e-c)(e-d)}. \quad \cdots \cdots \cdots \quad (2)$$

Selecting the points at equal intervals and letting

$$e-d=d-c=c-b=b-a=h,$$

and differentiation

$$y'_a=\frac{1}{12h}[-25y_a+48y_b-36y_c+16y_d-3y_e],$$

$$y'_b=\frac{1}{12h}[-3y_a-10y_b+18y_c-6y_d+y_e],$$

$$y'_c = \frac{1}{12h}[\quad y_a - 8y_b \qquad + 8y_d - y_e],$$

$$y'_d = \frac{1}{12h}[-\quad y_a + 6y_b - 18y_c + 10y_d + 3y_e],$$

$$y'_e = \frac{1}{12h}[\quad 3y_a - 16y_b + 36y_c - 48y_d + 25y_e].$$

Differentiating again

$$y''_a = \frac{1}{12h^2}[35y_a - 104y_b + 114y_c - 56y_d + 11y_e],$$

$$y''_b = \frac{1}{12h^2}[11y_a - 20y_b + 6y_c + 4y_d - y_e],$$

$$y''_c = \frac{1}{12h^2}[-y_a + 16y_b - 30y_c + 16y_d - y_e],$$

$$y'_d = \frac{1}{12h^2}[-y_a + 4y_b + 6y_c - 20y_d + 11y_e],$$

$$y'_e = \frac{1}{12h^2}[11y_a - 56y_b + 114y_c - 104y_d + 35y_e].$$

The results of applying these formulas to the function given are expressed in the table below.

x	y	y'	y''
1	.099833	.109451	− .001203
2	.208460	.107583	− .002524
3	.314566	.104415	− .003804
4	.416871	.099986	− .005045
5	.514136	.094347	− .006221
6	.605186	.087568	− .007322
7	.688921	.079733	− .008334
8	.764329	.070929	− .009258

These results agree fairly well with those previously obtained. It is probable that the formulas derived from the interpolation formula give the most satisfactory results.

As another application let us find the maximum or minimum value of a function having given three values near the critical point.

Let y_a, y_b, and y_c be three values of a function of x near its maximum or minimum corresponding to the values of x, a, b, and c respectively.

From (2)

$$y_x = y_a \frac{(x-b)(x-c)}{(a-b)(a-c)} + y_b \frac{(x-a)(x-c)}{(b-a)(b-c)} + y_c \frac{(x-a)(x-b)}{(c-a)(c-b)}.$$

Equating to zero the first derivative with respect to x

$$y'_x = y_a \frac{2x-b-c}{(a-b)(a-c)} + y_b \frac{2x-a-c}{(b-a)(b-c)} + y_c \frac{2x-a-b}{(c-a)(c-b)} = 0;$$

$$x = \frac{y_a(b^2-c^2) + y_b(c^2-a^2) + y_c(a^2-b^2)}{2[y_a(b-c) + y_b(c-a) + y_c(a-b)]}. \quad \ldots \quad \ldots \quad (6)$$

This is equivalent to drawing the parabola

$$y = A + Bx + Cx^2$$

through the three points and determining its maximum or minimum.

From the table of values

x	y
6.0	10.05
6.5	10.14
7.0	10.10

the abscissa of the maximum point is found from (6).

$$x = \frac{(10.05)(-6.75) + (10.14)(13) + (10.10)(-6.25)}{2[(10.05)(-.5) + (10.14)(1) + (10.10)(-.5)]} = 6.596$$

$$y = 10.1424.$$

CHAPTER VIII

NUMERICAL INTEGRATION

AREAS

An area bounded by the curve, $y = f(x)$, the axis of x, and two given ordinates is represented by the definite integral

$$A = \int_a^n y\,dx,$$

where the ordinates are taken at $x = a$ and $x = n$. It may be said that the definite integral represents the area under the curve, or that the area under the curve represents the value of the definite integral.

If a function is given by its graph, it is possible, by means of the planimeter, to find roughly the area bounded by the curve, two given ordinates and the x – axis, or, what amounts to the same thing, the area enclosed by a curve. This method is used in finding the area of the indicator diagrams of steam, gas or oil engines, and various other diagrams. The approximations in these cases are close enough to satisfy the requirements.

If, however, considerable accuracy is sought, or whenever the function is defined by a table of numerical values another method must be employed.

Mechanical Quadrature or Numerical Integration is the method of evaluating the definite integral of a function when the function is given by a series of numerical values. Even when the function is defined by an analytical expression but which cannot be integrated in terms of known functions by the method of the integral calculus, numerical integration must be resorted to for its evaluation.

The formulas employed in numerical integration are derived from those established for interpolation.

114

In interpolation it was found that the order of differences which must be taken into account depends upon the rapidity with which the differences decrease as the order increases. This is also true of numerical integration. It is the same as saying that if the series employed does not converge the process will give unsatisfactory results. An illustration will be given later.

Formulas for numerical integration will be derived from (1) of Chapter VII.

In this formula it was assumed that the ordinates are given at equal intervals.

$$y_x = y_0 + x\Delta y_0 + \frac{x(x-1)}{\underline{|2}}\Delta^2 y_0 + \frac{x(x-1)(x-2)}{\underline{|3}}\Delta^3 y_0$$

$$+ \frac{x(x-1)(x-2)(x-3)}{\underline{|4}}\Delta^4 y_0 + \frac{x(x-1)(x-2)(x-3)(x-4)}{\underline{|5}}\Delta^5 y_0$$

$$+ \frac{x(x-1)(x-2)(x-3)(x-4)(x-5)}{\underline{|6}}\Delta^6 y + \ldots \ldots \quad (1)$$

Integrating the right-hand member,

$$\int_0^n y_x dx = y_0 \int_0^n dx + \Delta y_0 \int_0^n x\,dx + \frac{\Delta^2 y_0}{\underline{|2}} \int_0^n x(x-1)dx$$

$$+ \frac{\Delta^3 y_0}{\underline{|3}} \int_0^n x(x-1)(x-2)dx$$

$$+ \frac{\Delta^4 y_0}{\underline{|4}} \int_0^n x(x-1)(x-2)(x-3)dx$$

$$+ \frac{\Delta_5 y_0}{\underline{|5}} \int_0^n x(x-1)(x-2)(x-3)(x-4)dx$$

$$+ \frac{\Delta^6 y_0}{\underline{|6}} \int_0^n x(x-1)(x-2)(x-3)(x-4)(x-5)dx + \ldots$$

$$= ny_0 + \frac{n^2}{2}\Delta y_0 + \left(\frac{n^3}{3} - \frac{n^2}{2}\right)\frac{\Delta^2 y_0}{\underline{|2}} + \left(\frac{n^4}{4} - n^3 + n^2\right)\frac{\Delta^3 y_0}{\underline{|3}} \cdot$$

$$+ \left(\frac{n^5}{5} - \frac{3n^4}{2} + \frac{11n^3}{3} - 3n^2\right)\frac{\Delta^4 y_0}{\underline{|4}}$$

$$+\left(\frac{n^6}{6}-2n^5+\frac{35}{4}n^4-\frac{50}{3}n^3+12n^2\right)\frac{\Delta^5 y_0}{\lfloor 5}$$

$$+\left(\frac{n^7}{7}-\frac{5}{2}n^6+17n^5-\frac{225}{4}n^4+\frac{274}{3}n^3-60n^2\right)\frac{\Delta^6 y_0}{\lfloor 6}+\cdots$$

The data given in any particular problem will enable us to compute the successive differences of y_0 up to $\Delta^n y_0$. On the assumption that all succeeding differences are so small as to be negligible the above formula gives an approximate value of the integral. It is only necessary to assign particular values to n.

Let $n=2$, then

$$\int_0^2 y_x dx = 2y_0 + 2\Delta y_0 + \tfrac{1}{3}\Delta^2 y_0,$$

$$\Delta y_0 = y_1 - y_0,$$

$$\Delta^2 y_0 = \Delta y_1 - \Delta y_0 = y_2 - y_1 - y_1 + y_0,$$

$$= y_2 - 2y_1 + y_0.$$

Substituting these values in the above integral it becomes

$$\int_0^2 y_x dx = 2y_0 + 2y_1 - 2y_0 + \tfrac{1}{3}y_2 - \tfrac{2}{3}y_1 + \tfrac{1}{3}y_0,$$

$$= \frac{y_0 + 4y_1 + y_2}{3}.$$

This is equivalent to assuming that the curve coincides with a parabola of the second degree.

If the common distance between the ordinates is h, the value becomes

$$\int_0^{2h} y dx = \tfrac{1}{3}h(y_0 + 4y_1 + y_2). \quad \cdots \quad (7)$$

If $n=3$

$$\int_0^3 y dx = 3y_0 + \tfrac{9}{2}\Delta y_0 + \tfrac{9}{4}\Delta^2 y_0 + \tfrac{3}{8}\Delta^3 y_0,$$

$$\Delta y_0 = y_1 - y_0,$$

$$\Delta^2 y_0 = \Delta y_1 - \Delta y_0 = y_2 - 2y_1 + y_0,$$

$$\Delta^3 y_0 = \Delta^2 y_1 - \Delta^2 y_0 = \Delta y_2 - \Delta y_1 - \Delta y_1 + \Delta y_0$$

$$= y_3 - 3y_2 + 3y_1 - y_0.$$

Substituting these values in the equations,

$$\int_0^3 y\,dx = 3y_0 + \tfrac{9}{2}y_1 - \tfrac{9}{2}y_0 + \tfrac{9}{4}y_2 - \tfrac{9}{2}y_1 + \tfrac{9}{4}y_0 + \tfrac{3}{8}y_3 - \tfrac{9}{8}y_2 + \tfrac{9}{8}y_1 - \tfrac{3}{8}y_0,$$

$$= \tfrac{3}{8}y_0 + \tfrac{9}{8}y_1 + \tfrac{9}{8}y_2 + \tfrac{3}{8}y_3,$$

$$= \tfrac{3}{8}(y_0 + 3y_1 + 3y_2 + y_3).$$

If the common distance between the ordinates is h the formula becomes

$$\int_0^{3h} = \tfrac{3}{8}h(y_0 + 3y_1 + 3y_2 + y_3). \quad \cdots \quad (8)$$

This is equivalent to assuming that the curve coincides with a parabola of the third degree.

If there are five equidistant ordinates, h representing the distance between successive ordinates

$$\int_0^{4h} y\,dx = \frac{14(y_0 + y_4) + 64(y_1 + y_3) + 24y_2}{45}h. \quad \cdots \quad (9)$$

If the area is divided into six parts bounded by seven equidistant ordinates the integral becomes

$$\int_0^6 y\,dx = 6y_0 + 18\Delta y_0 + 27\Delta^2 y_0 + 24\Delta^3 y_0 + \tfrac{123}{10}\Delta^4 y_0$$

$$+ \tfrac{33}{10}\Delta^5 y_0 + \tfrac{41}{140}\Delta^6 y_0.$$

Since the last coefficient, $\tfrac{41}{140}$, differs but slightly from $\tfrac{3}{10}$ and by the assumption that $\Delta^6 y_0$ is small the error will be slight if the last coefficient is replaced by $\tfrac{3}{10}$.

Doing this and replacing

Δy_0 by $y_1 - y_0$,

$\Delta^2 y_0$ by $y_2 - 2y_1 + y_0$,

$\Delta^3 y_0$ by $y_3 - 3y_2 + 3y_1 - y_0$,

$\Delta^4 y_0$ by $y_4 - 4y_3 + 6y_2 - 4y_1 + y_0$,

$\Delta^5 y_0$ by $y_5 - 5y_4 + 10y_3 - 10y_2 + 5y_1 - y_0$,

$\Delta^6 y_0$ by $y^6 - 6y_5 + 15y_4 - 20y_3 + 15y_2 - 6y_1 + y_0$,

gives the formula

$$\int_0^{6h} y\,dx = \tfrac{3}{10}h[y_0 + y_2 + y_4 + y_6 + 5(y_1 + y_5) + 6y_3]. \quad . \quad (10)$$

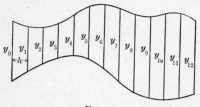

The application of these formulas is illustrated by finding the area in Fig. 27.

FIG. 27.

By (7)

$$A = \tfrac{1}{3}h(y_0 + 4y_1 + 2y_2 + 4y_3 + 2y_4 + 4y_5 + 2y_6 + 4y_7 + 2y_8 + 4y_9 + 2y_{10} + 4y_{11} + y_{12}).$$

By (8)

$$A = \tfrac{3}{8}h(y_0 + 3y_1 + 3y_2 + 2y_3 + 3y_4 + 3y_5 + 2y_6 + 3y_7 + 3y_8 + 2y_9 + 3y_{10} + 3y_{11} + y_{12}).$$

By (9)

$$A = \tfrac{1}{45}h[14(y_0 + 2y_4 + 2y_8 + y_{12}) + 64(y_1 + y_3 + y_5 + y_7 + y_9 + y_{11}) + 24(y_2 + y_6 + y_{10})].$$

By (10)

$$A = \tfrac{3}{10}h[y_0 + y_2 + y_4 + 2y_6 + y_8 + y_{10} + y_{12} + 5(y_1 + y_5 + y_7 + y_{11}) + 6(y_3 + y_9)].$$

1. A rough comparison of the approximations by the use of these formulas will be obtained by finding the value of $\int_1^{13} \dfrac{dx}{x}$. The value of this definite integral is $\log 13 = 2.565$. It is also equal to the area under the curve

$$y = \frac{1}{x}$$

from $x=1$ to $x=13$. Dividing the area up into 12 strips of unit width by 13 ordinates the corresponding values of x and y are

x	1	2	3	4	5	6	7	8	9	10	11	12	13
y	1	$\frac{1}{2}$	$\frac{1}{3}$	$\frac{1}{4}$	$\frac{1}{5}$	$\frac{1}{6}$	$\frac{1}{7}$	$\frac{1}{8}$	$\frac{1}{9}$	$\frac{1}{10}$	$\frac{1}{11}$	$\frac{1}{12}$	$\frac{1}{13}$

By (7)

$$A = \tfrac{1}{3}[1+2+\tfrac{2}{3}+1+\tfrac{2}{5}+\tfrac{2}{3}+\tfrac{2}{7}+\tfrac{1}{2}+\tfrac{2}{9}+\tfrac{2}{5}+\tfrac{2}{11}+\tfrac{1}{3}+\tfrac{1}{13}]$$

$$= 2.578, \text{ error } .5\%;$$

By (8), $\qquad A = 2.585$, error $.8\%$;

By (9), $\qquad A = 2.573$, error $.3\%$;

By (10), $\qquad A = 2.572$, error $.3\%$.

2. The accuracy of the approximation is much increased by taking the ordinates nearer together, as is shown by the following evaluation of

$$\int_0^1 \frac{dx}{1+x}.$$

The value of this integral is equal to the area under the curve

$$y = \frac{1}{1+x},$$

from $x=0$ to $x=1$. Dividing the area into twelve parts by thirteen equidistant ordinates the value of $\int_0^1 \frac{dx}{1+x}$ is found to be

By (7), 0.69314866, error 0.00000148;

By (8), 0.69315046, error 0.00000328;

By (9), 0.69314725, error 0.00000007;

By (10), 0.69314722, error 0.00000004.

The correct value is, of course, $\log_e 2$, which is 0.69314718.

Formulas (7) and (8) are Simpson's Rules, (10) is Weddle's Rule.

3. Apply the above formulas to the area of that part of the semi-ellipse included between the two perpendiculars erected at the middle points of the semi-major axes. Let this area be divided into twelve parts by equidistant ordinates.

Since the equation of the ellipse is

$$\frac{x^2}{a^2}+\frac{y^2}{b^2}=1,$$

these ordinates are

$$\tfrac{1}{2}\sqrt{3}\ b,\ \tfrac{1}{12}\sqrt{119}\ b,\ \tfrac{1}{3}\sqrt{8}\ b,\ \tfrac{1}{4}\sqrt{15}\ b,\ \tfrac{1}{6}\sqrt{35}\ b,\ \tfrac{1}{12}\sqrt{143}\ b,\ b,$$

$$\tfrac{1}{12}\sqrt{143}\ b,\ \tfrac{1}{6}\sqrt{35}\ b,\ \tfrac{1}{4}\sqrt{15}\ b,\ \tfrac{1}{3}\sqrt{8}\ b,\ \tfrac{1}{12}\sqrt{119}\ b,\ \tfrac{1}{2}\sqrt{3}\ b.$$

By (7), $A = 0.9566099ab$;

By (8), $A = 0.9566080ab$;

By (9), $A = 0.9566114ab$;

By (10), $A = 0.9566114ab$.

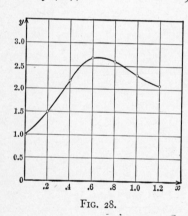

FIG. 28.

The correct value to seven places is $0.9566115ab$.

In the application of these formulas it is highly desirable to avoid large differences among the ordinates. For that reason the formulas do not give so good results when applied to the quadrant of the ellipse.

4. The area under the curve, Fig. 28, determined by the following sets of values:

x	0	.2	.4	.6	.8	1.0	1.2
y	1.0	1.5	2.2	2.7	2.6	2.3	2.1

is by (7)

$$A = \tfrac{1}{3}\cdot\tfrac{1}{5}(1.0+6.0+4.4+10.8+5.2+9.2+2.1) = 2.58,$$

and by (8),

$$A = \tfrac{3}{8}\cdot\tfrac{1}{5}(1.0+4.5+6.6+5.4+7.8+6.9+2.1) = 2.5725.$$

This area is represented by the definite integral $\int_0^{1.2} y\,dx$. The area found is therefore the approximate value of this integral

5. Find the area under the curve determined by the points

x	1	1.5	1.9	2.3	2.8	3.2	3.6	4.0	4.6	4.8	5.0
y	0	.40	1.08	1.82	2.06	2.20	2.30	2.25	2.00	1.80	1.5

The points located by the above sets of values are plotted in Fig. 29 and a smooth curve drawn through them. The area

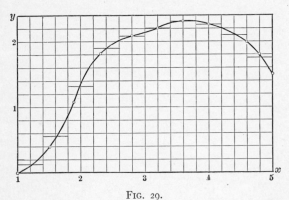

FIG. 29.

is divided into strips each having a width of .4. Rectangles are formed with the same area as the corresponding strips. The eye is a very good judge of the position of the upper boundary of each rectangle. Adding the lengths of these rectangles and multiplying the sum by .4 the area is found to be 6.644.

By Simpson's Rule, formula (7), are found

$$\text{for } h = .2, \quad A = 6.639,$$
$$h = .4, \quad A = 6.645.$$

The graphical determination of areas can be made to yield a close approximation by taking narrow strips, and where the points are given at irregular intervals the area can be found more rapidly than by the application of Simpson's Rules.

6. A gas expands from volume 2 to volume 10, so that its pressure p and volume v satisfy the equation $pv = 100$. Find the average pressure between $v = 2$ and $v = 10$.

The average pressure is equal to the work done divided by 8. The work is equal to the area under the curve $p = \dfrac{100}{v}$ from $v = 2$ to $v = 10$, which is

$$\int_2^{10} \frac{100}{v} dv = 100 \left[\log v \right]_2^{10} = 160.944.$$

That this area represents the work done in expanding the volume from 2 to 10 becomes evident in the following way. Let s represent the surface inclosing the gas, ps will then be the total pressure on that surface. The element of work will then be

$$dW = psdn,$$

when dn iepresents the element along the normal.

But
$$W = \int psdn.$$

and
$$sdn = dv,$$

$$W = \int pdv.$$

This is the equation above. The average pressure over the change of volume from 2 to 10 is

$$160.944 \div 8 = 20.118.$$

7. Find the mean value of $\sin^2 x$ from $x = 0$ to $x = 2\pi$. Plot the curve $y = \sin^2 x$ by the following values of x and y:

x	0	$\dfrac{\pi}{12}$	$\dfrac{\pi}{6}$	$\dfrac{\pi}{4}$	$\dfrac{\pi}{3}$	$\dfrac{5\pi}{12}$	$\dfrac{\pi}{2}$
y	0	.0670	.2500	.5000	.7500	.9330	1.0000

x	$\dfrac{7\pi}{12}$	$\dfrac{2\pi}{3}$	$\dfrac{3\pi}{4}$	$\dfrac{5\pi}{6}$	$\dfrac{11\pi}{12}$
y	.9330	.7500	.5000	.2500	.0670

x	π	$\dfrac{13\pi}{12}$	$\dfrac{7\pi}{6}$	$\dfrac{5\pi}{4}$	$\dfrac{4\pi}{3}$	$\dfrac{17\pi}{12}$	$\dfrac{3\pi}{2}$
y	0	.0670	.2500	.5000	.7500	.9330	1.0000

x	$\dfrac{19\pi}{12}$	$\dfrac{5\pi}{3}$	$\dfrac{7\pi}{4}$	$\dfrac{11\pi}{6}$	$\dfrac{23\pi}{12}$	2π
y	.9330	.7500	.5000	.2500	.0670	0

Applying Simpson's Rule, formula (7), the area is found to be π. The mean value is the area divided by 2π or .5.

8. A body weighing 100 lb. moves along a straight line without rotating, so that its velocity v at time t is given by the following table:

t sec............	1	3	5	7	9
v ft./sec........	1.47	1.58	1.67	1.76	1.86

Find the mean value of its kinetic energy from $t=1$ to $t=9$.

t............	1	3	5	7	9
v^2............	2.1609	2.4964	2.7889	3.0976	3.4596
Kinetic energy .	3.355	3.876	4.331	4.810	5.372

Plotting kinetic energy to t, the area under the curve is 34.755. This divided by 8 gives the mean kinetic energy as 4.357.

VOLUMES

Fig. 30 explains the application of the formulas to the problem of finding the approximate volume of an irregular figure. The area of the sections at right angles to the axis of x are:

$$A_1 = \tfrac{1}{3}k(y_1 + 4y_5 + y_4),$$

$$A_2 = \tfrac{1}{3}k(y_6 + 4y_9 + y_8),$$

$$A_3 = \tfrac{1}{3}k(y_2 + 4y_7 + y_3).$$

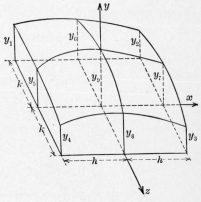

FIG. 30.

If the areas of these sections be looked upon as ordinates, h being the distance between two adjacent ones, it is evident that the volume may be represented by the area under the curve drawn through the extremities of these ordinates.

$$V = \tfrac{1}{3}h(A_1 + 4A_2 + A_3)$$

Substituting the values of A_1, A_2, and A_3 in this equation, the volume becomes

$$V = \tfrac{1}{3}h[\tfrac{1}{3}k(y_1 + 4y_5 + y_4) + \tfrac{4}{3}k(y_6 + 4y_9 + y_8) + \tfrac{1}{3}k(y_2 + 4y_7 + y_3)]$$

$$= \tfrac{1}{9}hk[y_1 + y_2 + y_3 + y_4 + 4(y_5 + y_6 + y_7 + y_8) + 16y_9]$$

In order to apply formulas (8), (9) and (10), the solid would have to be divided differently, but the method of application is at once evident from the above and needs no further discussion.

1. The following are values of the area in square feet of the cross-section of a railway cutting taken at intervals of 6 ft. How many cubic feet of earth must be removed in making the cutting between the two end sections given?

$$91, \qquad 95, \qquad 100, \qquad 102, \qquad 98, \qquad 90, \qquad 79.$$

These cross-section areas were obtained by the application of Simpson's Rules.

By (7),

$$V = \tfrac{1}{3} \cdot 6(91 + 380 + 200 + 408 + 196 + 360 + 79) = 3428;$$

By (8),

$$V = \tfrac{3}{8} \cdot 6(91 + 285 + 300 + 204 + 294 + 270 + 79) = 3426.8.$$

2. A is the area of the surface of the water in a reservoir when full to a depth h.

h ft....	30	25	20	15	10	5	0
A sq.ft..	26,700	22,400	19,000	16,500	14,000	10,000	5,000

Find (a) the volume of water in the reservoir, (b) the work done in pumping water out of the reservoir to a height of 100 ft. above the bottom until the remaining water has a depth of 10 ft.

$$V = \tfrac{5}{3}(26,700+89,600+38,000+66,000+28,000+40,000+5,000)$$

$$= 488,833 \text{ cu. ft.}$$

Work $= w \displaystyle\int_{10}^{30} A(100-h)dh$, where w = weight of 1 cu.ft. of water

= 62.3 lb. The value of this integral will be approximately the area under the curve determined by the points

h.........	30	25	20	15	10
$A(100-h)$.	1,869,000	1,680,000	1,520,000	1,402,500	1,260,000

multiplied by 62.3.

This area is equal to

$$\tfrac{5}{3}(1,869,000+6,920,000+3,040,000+5,610,000+1,260,000)$$

$$= 31,165,000.$$

Multiplying this by 62.3 gives the work equal to 1,941,579,500 ft.-lb.

3. When the curve in Fig. 29 revolves about the x-axis, find the volume generated.

The areas of the cross-sections corresponding to the given values of x are given in the following table:

x.....	0	.2	.4	.6	.8	1.0	1.2
A....	π	2.25π	4.84π	7.29π	6.76π	5.29π	4.41π

By (7) $V = 5.862\pi = 18.416$.

By (8) $V = 5.803\pi = 18.231$.

4. When the curve in Fig. 30 revolves about the x-axis, find the volume generated from $x = 1$ to $x = 4.2$. From the curve the following sets of values are obtained:

x	1.0	1.2	1.4	1.6	1.8	2.0	2.2	2.4	2.6
y	0	.11	.29	.53	.87	1.37	1.71	1.90	2.01
y^2	0	.012	.084	.281	.757	1.877	2.924	3.610	4.040
x		2.8	3.0	3.2	3.4	3.6	3.8	4.0	4.2
y		2.06	2.12	2.2	2.27	2.30	2.28	2.25	2.20
y^2		4.244	4.494	4.84	5.153	5.290	5.198	5.062	4.84

The volume is by (7)

$$\pi \cdot \tfrac{1}{3} \cdot \tfrac{1}{5}(149.004) = 31.2 \text{ cu. units.}$$

CENTROIDS

Let the coördinates of the centroid of an area be represented by $\bar{x}$ and $\bar{y}$. Then from the calculus

$$\bar{x} = \frac{\displaystyle\int_a^b xy\,dx}{\displaystyle\int_a^b y\,dx},$$

$$\bar{y} = \frac{\dfrac{1}{2}\displaystyle\int_a^b y^2\,dx}{\displaystyle\int_a^b y\,dx}.$$

The integral in the numerator of the value of $\bar{x}$ may be represented by the area bounded by the curve $Y = xy$, the x-axis and the two ordinates $x = a$ and $x = b$. The original area is bounded by the curve whose ordinates are represented by y, the x-axis and the two ordinates $x = a$ and $x = b$. The integral in the numerator of the value of $\bar{y}$ may be represented by the area bounded by the curve $Y = y^2$, the x-axis and the two ordinates $x = a$ and $x = b$.

For a volume generated by revolving a given area about the x-axis

$$\bar{x} = \frac{\pi \displaystyle\int_a^b y^2 x\,dx}{\pi \displaystyle\int_a^b y^2\,dx}.$$

When the volume is irregular

$$\bar{x} = \frac{\int_a^b A x dx}{\int_a^b A dx}.$$

The process of finding the coördinates of the centroid of the area in Fig. 28 is shown in the table:

x	0	.2	.4	.6	.8	1.0	1.2
y	1.0	1.5	2.2	2.7	2.6	2.3	2.1
xy	0.00	0.30	0.88	1.62	2.08	2.30	2.52
y^2	1.00	2.25	4.84	7.29	6.76	5.29	4.41
y^2x	0.000	0.450	1.936	4.374	5.408	5.290	5.292

The area under the curve $Y = xy$ is

$$\tfrac{1}{15}[0.00+1.20+1.76+6.48+4.16+9.20+2.52]=1.688;$$

$$\bar{x} = \frac{1.688}{2.58} = .654.$$

The area under the curve $Y = \tfrac{1}{2}y^2$ is

$$\tfrac{1}{30}[1.00+9.00+9.68+29.16+13.52+21.16+4.41]=2.931$$

$$\bar{y} = \frac{2.931}{2.58} = 1.136.$$

As was pointed out before, large changes in the ordinates must be avoided.

For the volume generated by revolving the area about the x-axis

$$\bar{x} = \frac{\pi\tfrac{1}{15}[0.000+1.800+3.872+17.496+10.816+21.160+5.292]}{\pi\tfrac{1}{15}[1.00+9.00+9.68+29.16+13.52+21.16+4.41]}$$

$$= \frac{60.436}{87.93} = .687.$$

MOMENTS OF INERTIA

The expression for the moment of inertia of an area about the y-axis is

$$I_y = \int_a^b x^2 y\, dx.$$

About the x-axis

$$I_x = \int_c^d x y^2 dy.$$

When the equation of the curve is known these integrals can be calculated at once, but when this is not the case approximate methods must be resorted to.

1. The process of finding the approximate values of these integrals is shown in the table below. The values of x and y are taken from Fig. 28.

x	0	.2	.4	.6	.8	1.0	1.2
y	1.0	1.5	2.2	2.7	2.6	2.3	2.1
$x^2 y$	0.000	0.060	0.335	0.972	1.664	2.300	3.024
$\frac{1}{3}y^3$	0.333	1.125	3.549	6.561	5.859	4.056	3.087

If the values of $x^2 y$ be plotted to x we will have a curve under which the area represents the moment of inertia of the area in Fig. 28 about the y-axis.

$$I_y = 1.357.$$

Dividing this by the area found before, there results for the radius of gyration about the y-axis

$$R_y^2 = .526.$$

Plotting $\frac{1}{3}y^3$ to x and finding the area under the curve so determined

$$I_x = 4.6136,$$

and

$$R_x^2 = 1.788.$$

2. The form of a quarter section of a hollow pillar, Fig. 31, is given by the following table. Find the moment of inertia of the section about the axes of x and y.

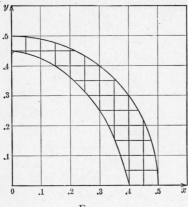

FIG. 31.

x	Y	x^2Y	y	X	y^2X
.00	.050	.00000	.00	.100	.00000
.05	.055	.00014	.05	.108	.00027
.10	.068	.00068	.10	.116	.00116
.15	.078	.00175	.15	.120	.00270
.20	.096	.00384	.20	.125	.00500
.25	.116	.00725	.25	.130	.00812
.30	.148	.01332	.30	.133	.01197
.35	.200	.02450	.35	.140	.01715
.40	.300	.04800	.40	.150	.02400
.45	.215	.04354	.45	.215	.04354
.50	.000	.00000	.50	.000	.00000

In the above table X stands for the width of the area parallel to the x-axis and Y for the width parallel to the y-axis. The area is 0.066.

The moment of inertia about the y-axis is

$$\int_0^{.5} x^2 Y\,dx = .00736;$$

$$R_y{}^2 = \frac{.00736}{.066} = 0.1115.$$

The moment of inertia about the x-axis is

$$\int_0^{.5} y^2 X dy = .00619;$$

$$R_x{}^2 = \frac{.00619}{.066} = 0.0938,$$

where R stands for the radius of gyration.

The values of the above integrals were computed by formula (7).

APPENDIX

If a chart could be constructed with all the different forms of curves together with their equations which may arise in representing different sets of data it would be a comparatively simple matter to select from the curves so constructed the one best suited for any particular set. Useful as such a chart would be its construction is clearly out of the question. The most that can be done of such a nature is to draw a number of curves represented by each one of the simpler equations.

A word of caution is, however, necessary here. A particular curve may seem to the eye to be the one best suited for a given set of data, and yet, when the test is applied, it may be found to be a very poor fit. It is of some aid, nevertheless, to have before the eye a few of the curves represented by a given formula.

The purpose of the following figures is to illustrate the changes in the form of curves produced by slight changes in the constants. Figs. I, II, III, and IV show changes produced by the addition of terms, Figs. V to XIX changes in form produced by changes in the values of the constants, and Fig. XX the changes in form brought about by varying both the values of the constants and the number of terms.

A discussion of all the figures is unnecessary. A few words in regard to one will suffice. Formula XIV, for example, $y = a + bx^c$, an equation which can be made to express fairly well the quantity of water flowing in many streams if x stands for mean depth and y for the discharge per second, represents a family of triply infinite number of curves. Fixing the values of b and c and varying the value of a does not change the form of the curve, but only moves it up or down

131

along the y-axis. Keeping the values of a and b constant and varying the value of c, the formula will represent an infinite number of curves all cutting the y-axis in the same point. In the same way, keeping the value of a and c constant and varying the value of b, an infinite number of curves is obtained, all of which cut the y-axis in a fixed point. In Fig. XIV the quantity a is constant and equal to unity, while b and c vary.

To one trained in the theory of curves the illustrations are, of course, of no essential value, but to one not so trained they may be of considerable help.

The text should be consulted in connection with the curves in any figure. The figures are designated to correspond to the formulas discussed in the first five chapters.

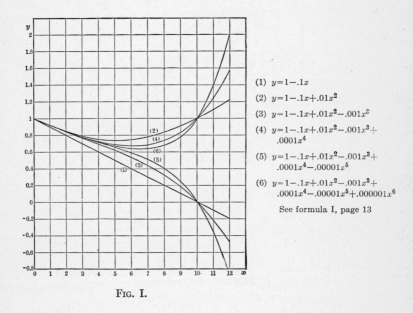

(1) $y=1-.1x$

(2) $y=1-.1x+.01x^2$

(3) $y=1-.1x+.01x^2-.001x^3$

(4) $y=1-.1x+.01x^2-.001x^3+$
$.0001x^4$

(5) $y=1-.1x+.01x^2-.001x^3+$
$.0001x^4-.00001x^5$

(6) $y=1-.1x+.01x^2-.001x^3+$
$.0001x^4-.00001x^5+.000001x^6$

See formula I, page 13

Fig. I.

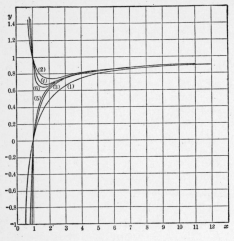

(1) $y=1-1/x$

(2) $y=1-1/x+1/x^2$

(3) $y=1-1/x+1/x^2-1/x^3$

(4) $y=1-1/x+1/x^2-1/x^3+1/x^4$

(5) $y=1-1/x+1/x^2-1/x^3+$
  $1/x^4-1/x^5$

(6) $y=1-1/x+1/x^2-1/x^3+$
  $1/x^4-1/x^5+1/x^6$

See formula II, page 22

FIG. II.

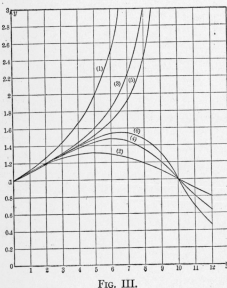

(1) $\dfrac{1}{y}=1-.1x$

(2) $\dfrac{1}{y}=1-.1x+.01x^2$

(3) $\dfrac{1}{y}=1-.1x+.01x^2-.001x^3$

(4) $\dfrac{1}{y}=1-.1x+.01x^2-.001x^3+$
  $.0001x^4$

(5) $\dfrac{1}{y}=1-.1x+.01x^2-.001x^3+$
  $.0001x^4-.00001x^5$

(6) $\dfrac{1}{y}=1-.1x+.01x^2-.001x^3+$
  $.0001x^4-.00001x^5+.000001x^6$

See formula III, page 25

FIG. III.

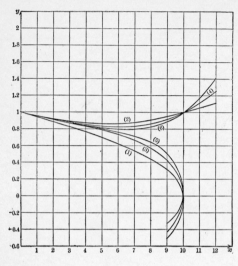

(1) $y^2 = 1 - .1x$

(2) $y^2 = 1 - .1x + .01x^2$

(3) $y^2 = 1 - .1x + .01x^2 - .001x^3$

(4) $y^2 = 1 - .1x + .01x^2 - .001x^3 + .0001x^4$

(5) $y^2 = 1 - .1x + .01x^2 - .001x^3 + .0001x^4 - .00001x^5$

(6) $y^2 = 1 - .1x + .01x^2 - .001x^3 + .0001x^4 - .00001x^5 + .000001x^6$

See formula IV, page 25

Fig. IV.

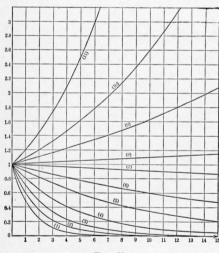

(1) $y = (.5)^x$

(2) $y = (.6)^x$

(3) $y = (.7)^x$

(4) $y = (.8)^x$

(5) $y = (.9)^x$

(6) $y = (.95)^x$

(7) $y = .99)^x$

(8) $y = (1.01)^x$

(9) $y = (1.05)^x$

(10) $y = (1.1)^x$

(11) $y = (1.2)^x$

See formula, V, page 27

Fig. V.

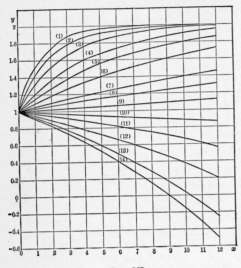

(1) $y=2-(.5)^x$
(2) $y=2-(.6)^x$
(3) $y=2-(.7)^x$
(4) $y=2-(.8)^x$
(5) $y=2-(.85)^x$
(6) $y=2-(.9)^x$ `
(7) $y=2-(.95)^x$
(8) $y=2-(.97)^x$
(9) $y=2-(.99)^x$
(10) $y=2-(1.01)^x$
(11) $y=2-(1.03)^x$
(12) $y=2-(1.05)^x$
(13) $y=2-(1.07)^x$
(14) $y=2-(1.08)^x$

See formula VI, page 28

FIG. VI.

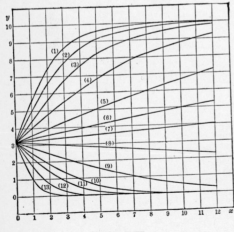

(1) $\log y=1-.5(.5)^x$
(2) $\log y=1-.5(.6)^x$
(3) $\log y=1-.5(.7)^x$
(4) $\log y=1-.5(.8)^x$
(5) $\log y=1-.5(.9)^x$
(6) $\log y=1-.5(.95)^x$
(7) $\log y=1-.5(.98)^x$
(8) $\log y=1-.5(1.02)^x$
(9) $\log y=1-.5(1.1)^x$
(10) $\log y=1-.5(1.2)^x$
(11) $\log y=1-.5(1.3)^x$
(12) $\log y=1-.5(1.5)^x$
(13) $\log y=1-.5(2)^x$

base$=10$

See formula VII, page 32

FIG. VII.

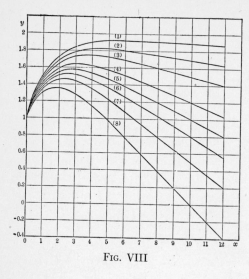

(1) $y = 2 - .01x - (.5)^x$

(2) $y = 2 - .03x - (.5)^x$

(3) $y = 2 - .05x - (.5)^x$

(4) $y = 2 - .08x - (.5)^x$

(5) $y = 2 - .1x - (.5)^x$

(6) $y = 2 - .12x - (.5)^x$

(7) $y = 2 - .15x - (.5)^x$

(8) $y = 2 - .2x - (.5)^x$

See formula VIII, page 33

FIG. VIII

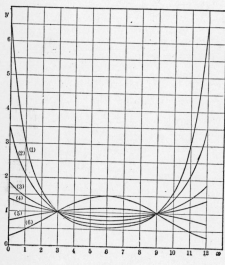

(1) $y = 10^{.81} - .36x + .03x^2$

(2) $y = 10^{.54} - .24x + .02x^2$

(3) $y = 10^{.27} - .12x + .01x^2$

(4) $y = 10^{.135} - .06x + .005x^2$

(5) $y = 10^{-.135} + .06x - 005x^2$

(6) $y = 10^{-.54} + .24x - .02x^2$

See formula IX, page 37

FIG. IX.

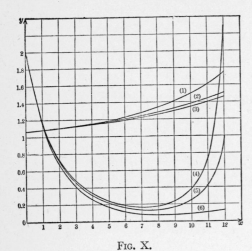

(1) $y = (1.01)^x (1.05)^{(1.2)^x}$

(2) $y = (1.01)^x (1.05)^{(1.16)^x}$

(3) $y = (1.01)^x (1.05)^{(1.15)^x}$

(4) $y = (.5)^x (2)^{(1.24)^x}$

(5) $y = (.5)^x (2)^{(1.23)^x}$

(6) $y = (.5)^x (2)^{(1.2)^x}$

See formula X, page 37

Fig. X.

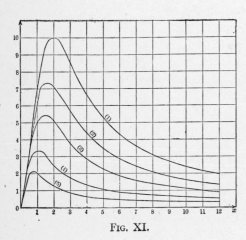

(1) $y = \dfrac{x}{.2 - .1x + .05x^2}$

(2) $y = \dfrac{x}{.2 - .1x + .07x^2}$

(3) $y = \dfrac{x}{.2 - .1x + .1x^2}$

(4) $y = \dfrac{x}{.2 - .1x + .2x^2}$

(5) $y = \dfrac{x}{.2 - .1x + .4x^2}$

See formula XI, page 38

Fig. XI.

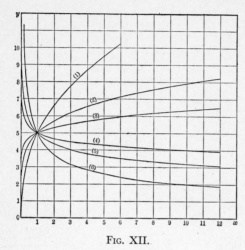

(1) $y = 5x^{.4}$

(2) $y = 5x^{.2}$

(3) $y = 5x^{.1}$

(4) $y = 5x^{-.1}$

(5) $y = 5x^{-.2}$

(6) $y = 5x^{-.4}$

See formula XII, page 42

Fig. XII.

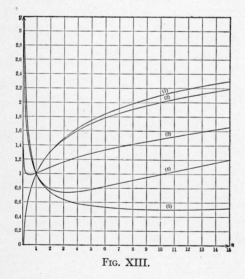

(1) $y = 1 + \log x + .1 \log^2 x;$
   $y = -1.5$ (min.) when $\log x = -5$

(2) $y = 1 + \log x + .01 \log^2 x;$
   $y = -24$ (min.) when $\log x = -50$

(3) $y = 1 + .2 \log x + .3 \log^2 x$

(4) $y = 1 - \log x + \log^2 x$

(5) $y = 1 - \log x + .5 \log^2 x$

See formula XIII, page 44

Fig. XIII.

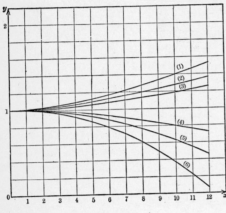

(1) $y = 1 + .008x^{1.7}$

(2) $y = 1 + .007x^{1.6}$

(3) $y = 1 + .006x^{1.5}$

(4) $y = 1 - .002x^2$

(5) $y = 1 - .003x^{2.1}$

(6) $y = 1 - .004x^{2.2}$

See formula XIV, page 45

Fig. XIV.

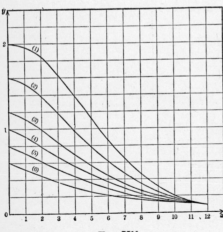

(1) $y = (2.0) \; 10^{-.01x^2}$

(2) $y = (1.6) \; 10^{-.02x^{1.7}}$

(3) $y = (1.2) \; 10^{-.03x^{1.5}}$

(4) $y = (1.0) \; 10^{-.04x^{1.36}}$

(5) $y = (0.8) \; 10^{-.05x^{1.24}}$

(6) $y = (0.6) \; 10^{-.06x^{1.12}}$

See formula XV, page 49

Fig. XV.

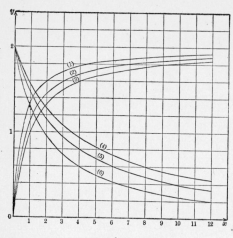

(1) $(y-2)(x-.5)=-1$

(2) $(y-2)(x+.75)=-1.5$

(3) $(y-2)(x+1)=-2$

(4) $(y+.1)(x+4)=8.2$

(5) $(y+.1)(x+3)=6.3$

(6) $(y+.1)(x+2)=4.2$

See formula XVI, page 53

Fig. XVI.

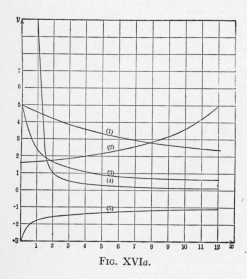

(1) $y=\tfrac{1}{2}\,10^{\frac{24}{x+24}}$

(2) $y=\tfrac{1}{2}\,10^{\frac{-12}{x-24}}$

(3) $y=\tfrac{1}{2}\,10^{\frac{2}{x+2}}$

(4) $y=\tfrac{1}{10}\,10^{\frac{2}{x}}$

(5) $y=-10^{\frac{.5}{x+1}}$

See formula XVIa, page 56

Fig. XVIa.

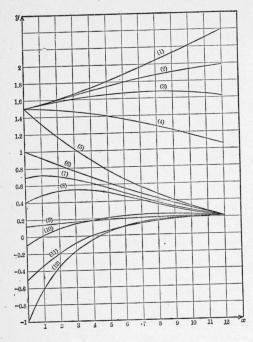

(1) $y = .5e^{.01x} + e^{.05x}$

(2) $y = 2e^{.05x} - .5e^{.1x}$

(3) $y = 2.25e^{.05x} - .75e^{.1x}$

(4) $y = 1.8e^{.01x} - .3e^{.1x}$

(5) $y = 1.92e^{-.1x} - .42e^{-.01x}$

(6) $y = 2e^{-.05x} - e^{-.01x}$

(7) $y = 4.2e^{-.2x} - 3.5e^{-.25x}$

(8) $y = 4.5e^{-.2x} - 4.1e^{-.25x}$

(9) $y = .25e^{-.01x} - .13e^{-.15x}$

(10) $y = e^{-.1x} - 1.1e^{-.2x}$

(11) $y = .27e^{-.01x} - .77e^{-.25x}$

(12) $y = e^{-.1x} - 2e^{-.25x}$

See formula XVII, page 58

Fig. XVII.

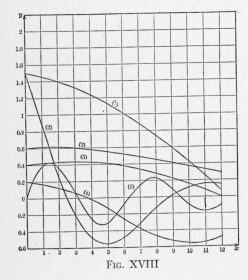

(1) $y = e^{.01x}(1.5 \cos .1x - .5 \sin .1x)$

(2) $y = e^{-.2x}(1.5 \cos .5x - .5 \sin .5x)$

(3) $y = e^{-.1x}(.6 \cos .1x + .8 \sin .1x)$

(4) $y = e^{.1x}(.2 \cos .3x - .1 \sin .3x)$

(5) $y = e^{.02x}(.4 \cos.16x + .17\sin.16x)$

(6) $y = .5e^{-.1x} \sin x$

See formula XVIII, page 61

Fig. XVIII

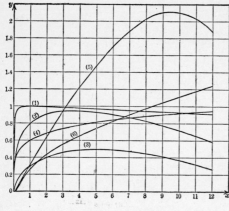

(1) $y = 2x^{.1} - x^{.2}$

(2) $y = 3x^{.5} - 2.2x^{.6}$

(3) $y = 2.3x^{.8} - 2x^{.85}$

(4) $y = .1x^{.1} + .5x^{.2}$

(5) $y = .33x - .0012x^3$

(6) $y = .25x^{.5} + .05x^{.8}$

See formula XIX, page 65

FIG. XIX.

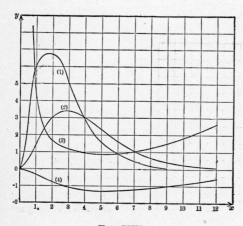

(1) $y = 15x^{1.5}(.4)^x$

(2) $y = 3x^2(.5)^x$

(3) $y = 3x^{-2}(1.5)^x$

(4) $y = -.5x^{1.5}(.75)^x$

See formula XIXa, page 72

FIG. XIXa.

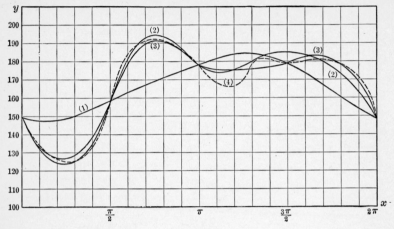

Fig. XX.

(1) $y = 166.25 - 14.5 \cos x - 2.75 \cos 2x - 10 \sin x$

(2) $y = 167.83 - 20 \cos x - 4.33 \cos 2x + 5.5 \cos 3x - 13.28 \sin x - 17.32 \sin 2x$

(3) $y = 167.62 - 17.5 \cos x - 2.75 \cos 2x + 3 \cos 3x - 1.38 \cos 4x - 12.42 \sin x - 18 \sin 2x - 2.42 \sin 3x$

(4) $y = 167.08 - 17.22 \cos x - 3.5 \cos 2x + 5.5 \cos 3x - 0.83 \cos 4x - 2.78 \cos 5x + 0.75 \cos 6x - 12.14 \sin x - 19.05 \sin 2x - \sin 3x - 1.73 \sin 4x + 1.14 \sin 5x$

See formula XX, page 74

INDEX

144